Science Plus ✚

SECOND EDITION

Published by HarperCollins*Publishers* Limited
77–85 Fulham Palace Road
Hammersmith
London
W6 8JB

Browse the complete Collins catalogue at
www.collinseducation.com

© HarperCollins*Publishers* Ltd 2004

10 9 8 7 6 5 4 3 2 1

ISBN 0 00 716077 1

Gareth Price and Martin Davies assert their moral
rights to be identified as the authors of this work.

British Library Cataloguing in Publication Data
A Catalogue record for this publication is available
from the British Library

Designed by Chi Leung
Project Management by Nicola Tidman
Picture research by Caroline Thompson
Illustrations by Phillip Burrows and Peter Harper
Production by Sarah Robinson
Printed and bound by Scotprint Haddington East
Lothian

1st edition writing team
Elizabeth Forth
Jenny Jones
Bob McDuell
Shirley Parsons
Gareth Price
Pamela Singh
Linda Welds

Illustrations from 1st edition by Barking Dog Art,
Russell Birkett, Tom Cross, Jerry Fowler

You may also like to visit:
www.harpercollins.co.uk
The book lover's website

Acknowledgements

Every effort has been made to contact the holders
of copyright material, but if any have been
inadvertently overlooked the publishers will be
pleased to make the necessary arrangements at
the first opportunity.

The publishers would like to thank the following for
permission to reproduce photographs (T = Top, B =
Bottom, C = Centre, L= Left, R = Right):

Advertising Archives, 6;
Anthony Blake Photo Library/Martin Brigdale, 29,
Patrick Syder, 32, James Murphy, 34BR;
Peter Roberts Collection/Neill Bruce, 56T;
Neill Bruce, 56C;
Illustration © Karen Carr, 13B;
Martyn Chillmaid, 13T, 34CR, 34CL, 47, 50L, 69;
Corbis/Jonathan Torgovnik, 39, Sandro Vannini, 40,
Bettmann, 43;
Getty Images/Clive Brunskill, 27, Pascal Rondeau,
50T;
Getty Images, 20, 36, 38, 51, 52, 53L, 55, 63, 65T,
65C, 66;
Ronald Grant Archive/Warner Bros, 7, 34T, 20th
Century Fox, 67;
Courtesy Kobal Collection/Paramount, 5, Universal,
12, Fox TV/Jerry Wolf, 17T, MGM, 59;
Andrew Lambert Photographic Collection, 30, 68C,
70B;
Military Picture Library/Peter Russell, 60;
Mountain Camera Picture Library/Leo Dickinson, 45;
NASA, 73BR;
NHPA/Andy Rouse, 14L, John Buckingham, 14R;
Natural History Museum Picture Library/De
Agostini, 13C;
PA Photos, 24, 37, 48;
Photofusion/Libby Welch, 10;
Popperfoto.com, 28;
Redferns/Mick Hutson, 26, 70T, Jon Super, 62;
Rex Features Ltd, 25, 41, 44, 49T, 64;
Science Photo Library, 18, Prof K Seddon & Dr T
Evans, Queen's University, Belfast, 15, Eric Grave,
17C, Manfred Kage, 19C, David M Martin, MD,
19T, 31TL, Peter Menzel, 53L, Kevin Beebe/Custom
Medical Stock Photo, 54, Jeremy Walker, 61, John
Mead, 68T, David Parker, 70C, NASA, 72, 73L, 75R,
75C, US Geological Survey, 75T;
© SHOUT, 4, 16, 46, 49C;
Still Pictures/Shehzad Noorani, 9;
C&S Thompson, 31TR;
Woodfall Wild Images/David Woodfall, 31B.

Cover image: Subatomic Particles - Science Photo
Library/Mehau Kulyk.

Contents

1.1 Is it murder?

Dead or alive? How can you tell? Can you tell just by looking or do you need complicated machines and years of training?

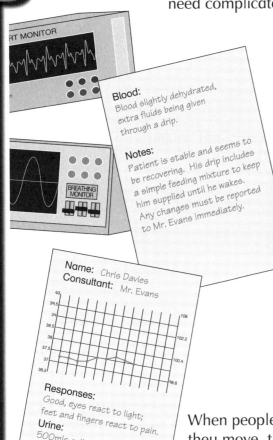

Blood:
Blood slightly dehydrated, extra fluids being given through a drip.

Notes:
Patient is stable and seems to be recovering. His drip includes a simple feeding mixture to keep him supplied until he wakes. Any changes must be reported to Mr. Evans immediately.

Name: Chris Davies
Consultant: Mr. Evans

Responses:
Good, eyes react to light; feet and fingers react to pain.
Urine:
500mls collected 10.34am ; bladder full

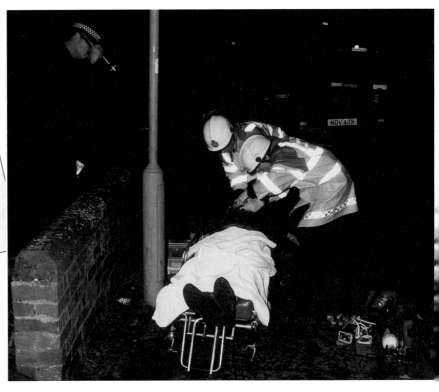

When people are alive they **breathe**, their blood **circulates**, they **grow**, they move, they eat, **digest** and **excrete** food and they may **reproduce**. They will also respond to the environment around them. If the body is not doing any of these things you can guess that the person is dead. These things that living creatures do are called **life processes**.

The body system	The main organ	Important life process
Respiratory	Lungs	Breathing
Circulatory	Heart and blood vessels	Blood circulation
Digestive	Stomach and intestines	Digest food
Excretory	Kidneys	Filter waste products from the blood
Reproductive	Ovaries and testes	Produce babies

1 List the things that show you a person is alive.
2 What does the information in the charts above tell you about Chris Davies' condition?
3 List *all* of the processes that go on in a living body.
4 How can you tell that each process is working?

breathing	circulation	growth	digestion
excretion	reproduce	life process	

1.2 Bones?

'It's life Jim ... but not as we know it!' How can Bones treat weird aliens from outer space? He's looking for the same life processes that he finds in humans. When he finds these he can guess at what might be wrong.

Different parts of the body do different jobs. Doctors can remove damaged body parts and replace them with something that does the job properly. For example, a metal pin in your leg can do the job of a bone.

Sometimes the replacement part comes from another person. The person who gives the organs is called the **donor**. They carry a donor card. After we die the organs in our body can be kept alive for a short while. While the organs are still alive they can be **transplanted** into another person. The person who gets the organs is called the **host**. Donors need to be matched to hosts. This stops the host's body rejecting the new organ.

When we die our bodies start to **decay**. After a short while the body parts cannot be used for transplants. Doctors often keep the body cool to reduce the speed of decay.

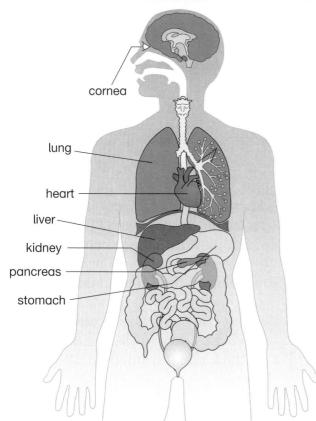

Donor organ	Cannot be used after:
Heart	7 hours
Liver	7 hours
Pancreas	30 hours
Kidney	72 hours
Cornea	Collected within 24 hours and put in eyebank

1 List six body parts that can be transplanted.
2 How are the removed organs kept in good condition?
3 Why do some people have transplant operations?
4 What does the word donor mean?
5 Which organ lasts the longest?
6 Write down two problems with transplant operations.

| **donor** | **transplant** | **host** | **decay** |

5

1.3 Fast reactions

DO NOT UNDERESTIMATE THE POWER OF PLAYSTATION

How good are you at computer games? In many computer games you have to **react** quickly to unexpected events on the screen. You decide what to do to defeat the alien or pilot the spaceship. Computer game designers work hard to make sure their games keep us stimulated and active.

A **stimulus** is something which makes people react. What we do is called a **reaction**. So, when we hear our phone ringing we pick it up to answer it.

Humans also have very fast reactions to some stimuli, such as a hot plate or a loud sound. We call these special reactions **reflexes**. For example, if dust gets up your nose, you sneeze. This stops the dust going down into your lungs. Reflexes protect us from harm. We don't have to think about what to do. We just react.

1　List three stimuli that you respond to.
2　How do you react to these stimuli?
3　What is a reflex reaction?
4　List three reflexes.
5　Plan an investigation to test your reaction speed.

| react | stimulus | reaction | reflex |

1.4 The reanimator!

Death and decay happen. We cool food and body organs to slow down the speed of decay. We cannot do this to live humans! We have to wait until they are dead. Some people have their heads frozen when they die. They hope that one day they can have a new body built back onto it!

Bodies are built of **cells**. There are probably over a million, million cells in each of us. There are many different types of cell in the body. These cells look very different but they all have a **nucleus**, **cytoplasm** and a **cell membrane**.

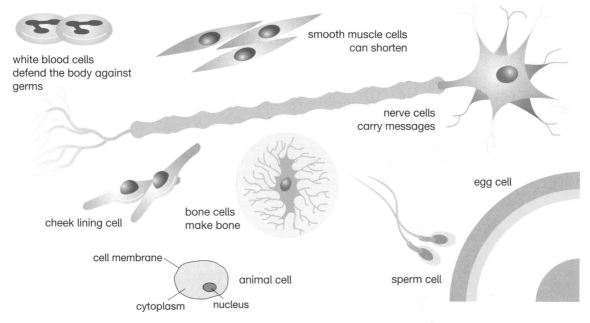

white blood cells defend the body against germs

smooth muscle cells can shorten

nerve cells carry messages

cheek lining cell

bone cells make bone

egg cell

sperm cell

cell membrane

animal cell

cytoplasm   nucleus

Cells are very delicate. The membrane is thin. Sharp ice crystals form in the cell when it freezes. The crystals can burst the membrane. Freezing cells is difficult. Freezing whole bodies must be even harder!

1 What is a cell?
2 Draw and label a cell.
3 Name some human cells and say what they do.
4 What is the problem with trying to freeze cells?
5 Draw diagrams to show what happens when a cell freezes.

| cell | nucleus | cytoplasm | cell membrane |

2.1 Reproduction

The parts of the male and female reproductive systems that we can see outside the body are called **genitals**. They are only part of the body structures needed to produce babies.

The other structures are located inside the body. These stuctures and their functions are shown in the diagram and table below.

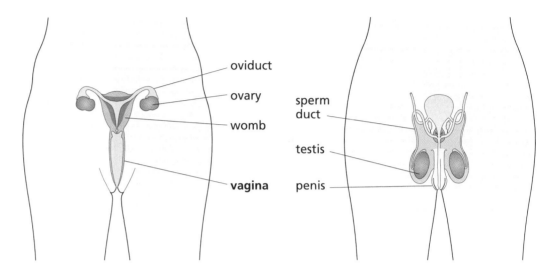

Reproductive organ	Function
Ovary	Produces the **egg**. Waves of fluid carry the egg along the oviduct towards the womb.
Oviduct	Carries the egg to the womb. The sperm **fertilises** the egg in the oviduct.
Womb	A muscular bag where the baby develops.
Testis	Produces **sperm** cells.
Sperm duct	Carries the sperm from the testes to the **penis**.

When the egg is fertilised by the sperm, the sperm and egg cells fuse. This new cell then travels to the womb where it develops into a baby.

1 Which part of the man produces sperm?
2 Which part of the woman produces the egg?
3 Where do the sperm and egg meet?
4 What happens when the sperm fertilises the egg?

genitals	**vagina**	**ovary**	**egg**	**oviduct**	**fertilise**
womb	**testis**	**sperm**	**sperm duct**	**penis**	

2.2 A pause for pregnancy

This antenatal clinic was opened in New Delhi a few years ago and the benefits can already be seen. **Antenatal** means 'before birth' and people come to the clinic when they know they are pregnant. The people who work at the clinic offer advice and some simple medicines to keep the mothers-to-be healthy during their pregnancy. This results in healthier mothers and healthier babies.

When a woman becomes pregnant, her periods stop and she begins to gain weight. The woman's doctor, or workers at the antenatal clinic, will take measurements to check that the baby is growing properly inside her. They take **blood pressure**, **weight** and **height** during the whole 9 months of the pregnancy. They can even test the mother's urine for chemicals which might show that the baby is in trouble. Once the baby has been born, the mother begins to lose weight and her periods start again.

DATE OF CONFINEMENT...... 8/6/02 ......
PREGNANCY MATURITY...... 40+6 ......WEEKS
LABOUR 1st stage...... 12hrs 45mins ......
 2nd stage...... 1hr 40mins ......
 3rd stage...... 5mins ......
TOTAL DURATION...... 14hrs 30mins ......
METHOD OF DELIVERY
Placenta and membranes complete
Blood loss 300mls.
SEX:(MALE) FEMALE (ring as appropriate)
BIRTH MASS...... 3350 ......g
DISCHARGE MASS...... 3600 ......g
METHOD OF FEEDING...... Breast ......
POST NATAL CARE HOSPITAL /(GP)

PREFERRED HOSPITAL...........................
PREFERRED CONSULTANT...................

ANTENATAL RECORD

Date	Last period (weeks)	Can you hear baby's heart?	Urine tests		Blood pressure	Mass (kg)
			Glucose	Protein		
27/10/01	9			NAD	125/70	
16 Nov	11+6			NAD	100/60	48.2
8/12/01	(14+4)	FMF	NAD	NAD	115/60	50kg
6.1.02	19 wks	FMF	NAD	NAD	110/60	52kg
1 Jan 02	19+5		NAD	NAD	130/70	55.3
2.2.02	23	H	NAN	NAN	115/60	54 K
Mar 02	27+	FMF	NIL			
3/3/02	28⁴	FMF				

1 What does an antenatal clinic do?
2 How long does a baby need to stay inside its mother before it is ready to be born?
3 For how long was this mother in labour?
4 How much did the baby weigh when it was born?

| **antenatal** | **blood pressure** | **weight** | **height** |

2.3 Birth

They said it would start during the night – and they were right! I had gone to bed and was trying to sleep when the first **contraction** came. It didn't really hurt but it was enough to keep me awake. I knew the contraction was the muscles tensing, getting ready to push the baby out. But I also knew that it was only the first sign – a lot more had to happen first.

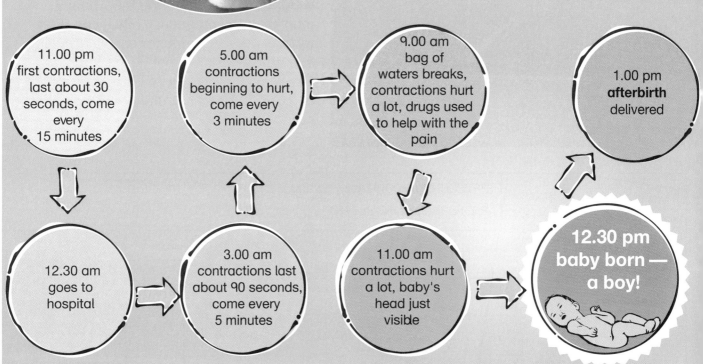

11.00 pm
first contractions, last about 30 seconds, come every 15 minutes

5.00 am
contractions beginning to hurt, come every 3 minutes

9.00 am
bag of waters breaks, contractions hurt a lot, drugs used to help with the pain

1.00 pm
afterbirth delivered

12.30 am
goes to hospital

3.00 am
contractions last about 90 seconds, come every 5 minutes

11.00 am
contractions hurt a lot, baby's head just visible

12.30 pm
baby born — a boy!

1 How long does it take from the start of labour to the baby being born?
2 How long after labour starts did the mother need drugs for the pain?
3 What is a contraction?
4 What do contractions do?
5 Design a leaflet that explains what happens during labour. In your leaflet try to give some suggestions of things the partner can do to help reassure the mother.

contraction   afterbirth

2.4 Your turn!

A new baby in the home creates a lot of work. Changing nappies, feeding, cleaning up sick ... it's all such fun! And for mum this all happens after the birth, which can be exhausting and even dangerous. So how can dad help out?

All the time the baby is growing and changing. So as time goes on the family has to change again!

To make sure that the baby is healthy and growing properly, the mum and her baby visit a health clinic regularly. Here, a nurse records the baby's weight gain and any comments on a card, like the one shown below.

WEIGHT RECORD (birth to 2 yrs)

Date	Weight	Weight gain	Comments
9/2/02	3.82kg	birth weight	
20/2/02	4.50kg	0.68kg	
19/3/02	4.95kg	0.45kg	reflexes ok
16/4/02	5.12kg	0.17kg	small weight gain
14/5/02	5.54kg	0.42kg	
11/6/02	5.95kg		hearing, sight ok

1 Sort the jobs in the pictures above into three lists. Things that only mum can do, things that only dad can do, things that both parents could do.
2 Use the information in baby Joe's card to plot a graph of his weight gain.
3 Why is there no figure for weight gain for the 9th of February?
4 What is the weight gain for the 11th of June?
5 Why do you think the health visitor has made a note by the record for the 16th April?

birth weight   reflex   hearing   sight

3.1 Making fossils

Dinosaurs leave behind the biggest **fossils**. Sometimes they are bones or teeth, sometimes they are piles of dinosaur faeces! The faeces show scientists what the dinosaurs ate. Scientists have even found fossil dinosaur footprints on river banks and fossils of dinosaur eggs. But how are fossils created in the first place?

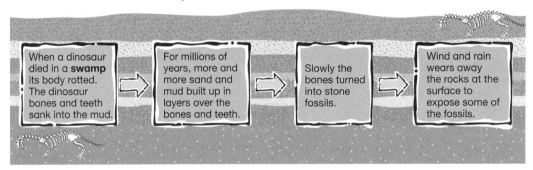

When a dinosaur died in a **swamp** its body rotted. The dinosaur bones and teeth sank into the mud.

For millions of years, more and more sand and mud built up in layers over the bones and teeth.

Slowly the bones turned into stone fossils.

Wind and rain wears away the rocks at the surface to expose some of the fossils.

The real **Jurassic** Park was in Texas 200 million years ago. Many different types of dinosaur lived there. We know this because of the fossils found in the rocks. Not all of the dinosaurs were alive at the same time. The oldest rocks contain the oldest fossils. Usually, older rocks are underneath younger ones. We can tell the age of a rock, and the fossil it contains, by how deeply it is buried and the radioactive chemicals that it contains.

1 List the main things that must happen for a fossil to be formed.
2 Draw a cliff showing the layers of rock.
3 On your cliff diagram, label the oldest layer.
4 On your cliff diagram, label the layer that will have the youngest fossils.
5 Give two ways to decide the age of a rock.

dinosaur   **fossil**   **swamp**   **Jurassic**

3.2 Dino shapes

How do we know what dinosaurs looked like? No-one has ever actually seen them. The fossils left behind give us clues. A modern day meat-eater has sharp teeth and large jaws. If we find a dinosaur jaw bone with many sharp teeth we can assume that it came from a meat-eater. Large claws also suggest that the dinosaur was a meat-eater. The claws would have been used for hunting and killing its prey.

Tyrannosaurus was a hunter with powerful muscles and sharp teeth and claws. **Ichthyosaurus** was a dinosaur that swam like a fish. It had a smooth body to move through the water easily. These differences are called **adaptations** because they adapt the dinosaurs to the places where they live.

Even dinosaurs of the same type would be slightly different from each other. One tyrannosaurus might be slightly taller, or stronger than all the others living in that area. He would be a better hunter and so get more food. He might be more likely to survive and breed to produce stronger, taller dinosaurs. Over millions of years these changes might lead to a completely new sort of dinosaur.

1 List the adaptations that the ichthyosaurus had for life in water.
2 List the adaptations that the **apatosaurus** had for life on land.
3 List the adaptations that the tyrannosaurus had for life as a hunter.
4 How do you think a longer neck would help an apatosaurus to survive?
5 How do you think being able to run faster would help a tyrannosaurus to survive?

tyrannosaurus ichthyosaurus adaptation apatosaurus

3.3 Last chance to see...

The dinosaurs died out hundreds of millions of years ago, and we are still not certain why. They were very successful animals. Some of the biggest and fiercest hunters that have ever lived were dinosaurs. Some of the largest plant-eaters ever were dinosaurs. What went wrong? Why did they become **extinct**?

Some scientists suggest a giant meteorite hit the Earth. It created tidal waves and filled the air with dust and smoke. The dust blocked out the sunlight and the Earth's climate became colder. The dinosaurs could not survive the change in their **environment** and slowly died out.

These days, humans are probably the biggest threat to animals and plants. We are changing their environment and they may not be able to survive. Animals that are **adapted** to life in the jungle are dying as the rainforests are cleared. Animals adapted to cold are dying as the Earth gets hotter due to global warming. Deserts are increasing in size, so plants and animals that cannot survive drought are dying out. Humans also hunt rare species of animal, often for their meat or fur.

1 What may have caused the dinosaurs to die out?
2 Why can any change lead to problems for some animals and plants?
3 What does the word extinct mean?
4 Give three things that human beings are doing to make the world more dangerous for other animals and plants.

| extinct | environment | adapted |

3.4 From genes to giants

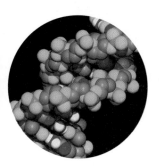

The **cells** in your body contain **genes**. Genes control the way you grow and develop. If you have blue eyes it is because you have the genes for blue eyes. The **nucleus** of a cell contains its store of genes. Genes are small parts of a complicated chemical called **DNA**. DNA is shaped like two interlinked spirals.

Since genes control how living things grow, it should be possible to use dinosaur genes to grow a dinosaur. But where can we find dinosaur genes?

Making dinosaurs for Jurassic Park

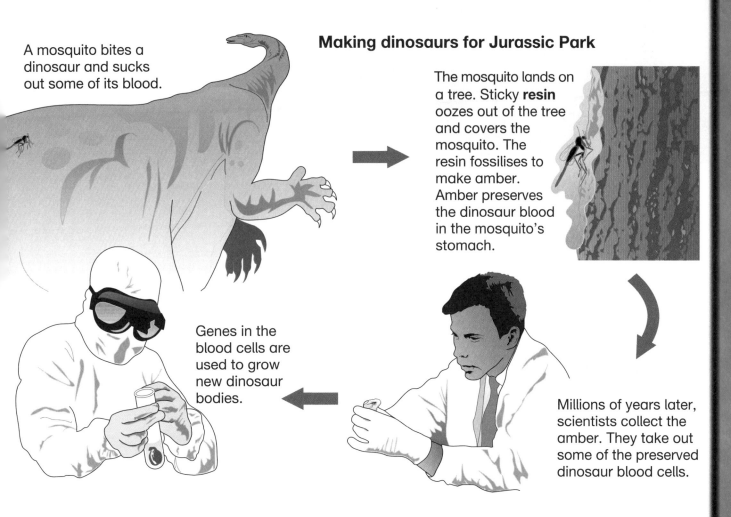

A mosquito bites a dinosaur and sucks out some of its blood.

The mosquito lands on a tree. Sticky **resin** oozes out of the tree and covers the mosquito. The resin fossilises to make amber. Amber preserves the dinosaur blood in the mosquito's stomach.

Genes in the blood cells are used to grow new dinosaur bodies.

Millions of years later, scientists collect the amber. They take out some of the preserved dinosaur blood cells.

1 Where did the scientists in the film *Jurassic Park* get dinosaur genes?
2 What preserved the dinosaur blood?
3 If a mosquito sucked human blood what genes would it have in its stomach?
4 List the reasons why people should try to recreate extinct dinosaurs.
5 List the reasons why people should not try to recreate extinct dinosaurs.

cell	gene	nucleus	DNA	resin

4.1 Save a life!

You can save a life here – if you know what to do! A person cannot live without **oxygen** for more than three minutes. When we stop **breathing** we stop taking in oxygen. The blood carries oxygen from the lungs to other parts of the body. If the heart stops beating then the blood cannot flow. You could die!

Casualty

➕ **1 Assess the situation**
Find out what happened and who is injured.

➕ **2 Make safe**
Make sure that the person is no longer in danger and that no-one else is going to get hurt.

➕ **3 Give emergency first aid (ABC code)**
a **Airways** – check that they are open. Remove a blockage if necessary.
b **Breathing** – check to see if the casualty is breathing. Give the kiss of life if necessary.
c **Circulation** – is the heart still beating? If yes, then check for signs of **bleeding**. Stop the flow of blood.

➕ **4 Get help**
Get qualified help. Dial 999 for an ambulance. If possible, someone should stay with the casualty.

1 Why is it important that the casualty keeps breathing?
2 Why is it important that the heart keeps beating?
3 Write out the three stages of emergency first aid.
4 Why is it important to make sure that the area is safe?
5 List the information you would need to give if you dialled 999.

| oxygen | breathing | airways | circulation | bleeding |

4.2 What do you want? Blood?

Blood is great stuff! It keeps us alive by transporting oxygen and food around the body. It also carries carbon dioxide to the lungs to be breathed out. Cells in the blood also help to protect against germs. However, to protect against vampires you need garlic, sunlight or silver crucifixes! Blood just makes it worse!

Red bone marrow makes **red blood cells**. Red blood cells pick up oxygen in the lungs and carry it around the body. These unusual cells do not have a nucleus and die after about 100 days.

Plasma is the liquid part of the blood. It is a pale yellow solution of sugar, salt and many other substances.

There are many different types of **white blood cells**. They all help to protect the body from disease.

Platelets are very small particles in the blood. They help the blood to clot.

1 What do red blood cells do?
2 What do white blood cells do?
3 Which part of the blood helps it to clot?
4 List the things in plasma.
5 Carry out a survey to find out how many people have had an injury involving loss of blood.

| red blood cells | white blood cells | plasma | platelets |

4.3 Heartbeat

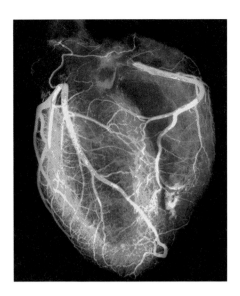

This heart could save a life. Until a very short time ago it was beating inside someone else who died in a car accident. He carried a donor card which said that he wanted to help someone after he had died.

His heart will soon be beating in another person's chest. This person's own heart has been damaged by infection and no longer works properly. Without this transplant they will die. But why is the heart so important?

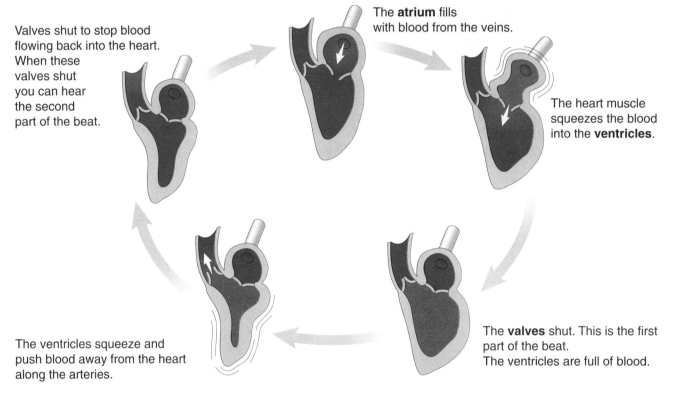

Valves shut to stop blood flowing back into the heart. When these valves shut you can hear the second part of the beat.

The **atrium** fills with blood from the veins.

The heart muscle squeezes the blood into the **ventricles**.

The ventricles squeeze and push blood away from the heart along the arteries.

The **valves** shut. This is the first part of the beat. The ventricles are full of blood.

The heart is made of muscle and is really two pumps stuck together. The left side pumps blood from the body to the lungs. The right side takes blood from the lungs and pumps it to the body. In the lungs the blood loses carbon dioxide and gains oxygen. We breathe out the **carbon dioxide**. The blood carries the **oxygen** to other parts of the body.

1　Where does blood enter the heart?
2　How many sets of valves are there in each side of the heart?
3　List the parts of the heart.
4　What happens to the blood in the lungs?

| valve | atrium | ventricle | carbon dioxide |
| oxygen | | | |

4.4 Arteries and veins

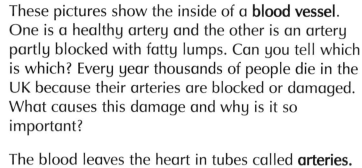

These pictures show the inside of a **blood vessel**. One is a healthy artery and the other is an artery partly blocked with fatty lumps. Can you tell which is which? Every year thousands of people die in the UK because their arteries are blocked or damaged. What causes this damage and why is it so important?

The blood leaves the heart in tubes called **arteries.** The arteries divide into smaller and smaller tubes. The smallest tubes are called **capillaries**. These are so small you cannot see them without a microscope. The capillaries link up into larger and larger tubes to take blood back to the heart. These tubes are called **veins**.

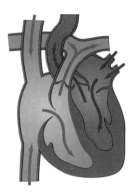

As we get older our hearts begin to weaken.

Smoking damages the lungs. Chemicals in cigarette smoke also make the heart beat more quickly all the time.

Lack of **exercise** means muscles go flabby. Since the heart is a muscle it can get weaker if it becomes unfit. Exercise encourages the heart to grow and develop.

People who are overweight put a strain on their heart. The blood has to travel further around their body than in thinner people.

Sometimes a fatty substance coats the inside walls of blood vessels. This makes the blood vessel narrower. The heart has to work much harder to pump blood along it.

1 List the things that can damage your heart.
2 Sort your list into things we can prevent and those that we cannot do anything about.
3 Describe ways to prevent your heart being damaged.
4 Plan an investigation to find out how different sorts of exercise affect your heart rate.
5 Design a poster for the wall of a sports centre telling people how to look after their heart. Think about all the different people who will see the poster: old and young, male and female.

blood vessel   artery   capillary   vein   exercise

Building bodies

5.1 Special bodies

We are what we eat. Our bodies are mainly made up of water, but also contain **carbohydrates**, **protein**, **fat**, **vitamins** and **minerals**. We use our food to build us up and give us **energy**. The food we eat is called our **diet**. If there is something wrong with our diet there will be something wrong with our body. Of course, different people need different diets!

Carbohydrates
Give the body energy
- sugars
- bread
- vegetables

Vitamins and minerals
A collection of different chemicals needed in very small amounts. They affect many different parts of the body.
- green vegetables and fruit
- milk and milk products

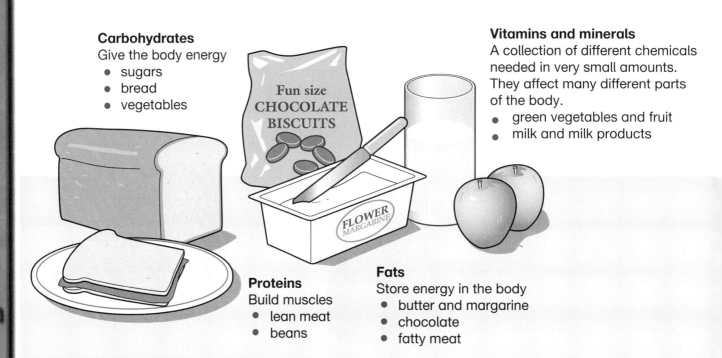

Proteins
Build muscles
- lean meat
- beans

Fats
Store energy in the body
- butter and margarine
- chocolate
- fatty meat

1 List the foods you think a Sumo wrestler would eat.
2 List the foods you think a body builder would eat.
3 List the food you ate yesterday.
4 Sort your food into carbohydrates, fats and proteins.
5 Give two ways you could improve your diet.

carbohydrate	protein	fat	vitamins	minerals
energy	diet			

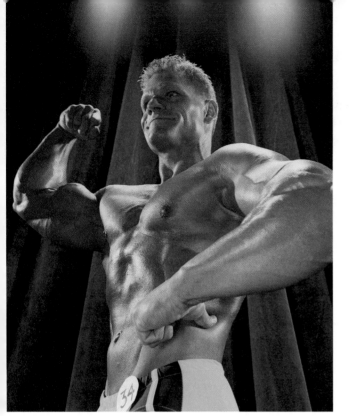

5.2 Label lore

Most foods are a **mixture** of different food types. Chicken has lots of **protein** and little **fat**. Beef has lots of protein but more fat. A body builder needs the protein but not the fat, so will eat more chicken. Body builders spend a lot of time reading food labels!

Food labels give us **nutritional** information. Many dieters look for the **energy** content of the food on the label. They try to avoid foods with lots of energy. This means they start to use up their stored fat and they lose weight. They need to be careful that they get enough of the food groups like proteins and vitamins and minerals or they can become ill.

4 STEWING STEAKS

Typical values per 100g (3.5oz)

ENERGY	223kcal, 932kJ
PROTEIN	13.9g
CARBOHYDRATE	0.0g
FATS	11.0g

Skinless Frozen Chicken

Typical values per 100g (3.5oz)

ENERGY	210kcal, 880kJ
PROTEIN	33.2g
CARBOHYDRATE	0.0g
FATS	5.4g

Chocolate Biscuit (KitKat)
Typical values per 100g
ENERGY 503kcal, 2103kJ
PROTEIN 7.6g
CARBOHYDRATE 59.1g
FATS 26.2g

INGREDIE
HYDROGE
WHEY PO
FLAVOUR
ETABLE
THIS P

Roasted Salted Peanuts

Typical values per 100g
ENERGY 600kcal, 2489kJ
PROTEIN 29.0g
CARBOHYDRATE 8.6g
FATS 50.0g

1 Almost all foods are mixtures. Explain what the word mixture means.
2 Is it a good idea to eat a diet with only one type of food? Why?
3 Sort the foods shown above so that the one with the most protein comes first.
4 Draw a bar chart to show the carbohydrate, fat and protein in chicken. You could draw another one for beef.
5 Why do body builders eat a high protein diet?

| mixture | protein | fat | nutrition | energy |

5.3 This takes guts!

Food must be digested before it is **absorbed**. **Digestion** means to break the food down into smaller particles. Digesting food takes guts! **Gut** is the scientific name for the tube that takes food from our mouth to our **anus**. As food travels along the tube it is broken down and absorbed by the body.

The body produces **digestive enzymes** to break down large food molecules into smaller ones. These smaller molecules pass through the wall of the gut into the body.

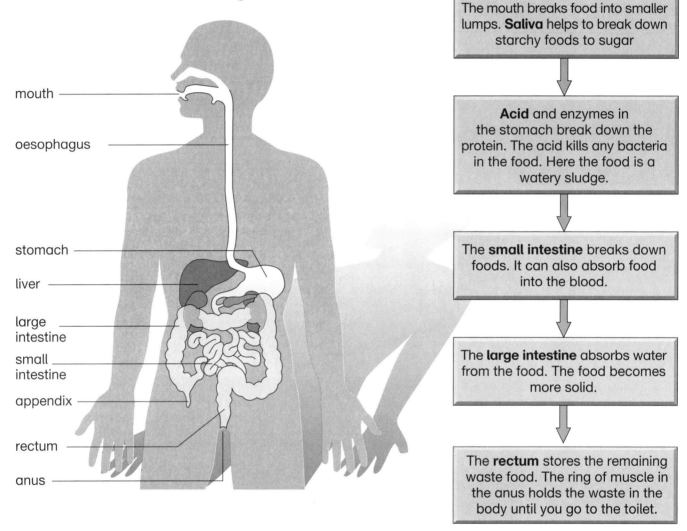

The mouth breaks food into smaller lumps. **Saliva** helps to break down starchy foods to sugar

Acid and enzymes in the stomach break down the protein. The acid kills any bacteria in the food. Here the food is a watery sludge.

The **small intestine** breaks down foods. It can also absorb food into the blood.

The **large intestine** absorbs water from the food. The food becomes more solid.

The **rectum** stores the remaining waste food. The ring of muscle in the anus holds the waste in the body until you go to the toilet.

mouth
oesophagus
stomach
liver
large intestine
small intestine
appendix
rectum
anus

1 List the parts of the gut that food passes through from the mouth to the anus.
2 What do digestive enzymes do?
3 Draw an outline of the gut. Colour the parts that break food down in red.
4 Colour the parts of the gut that absorb water in blue.
5 Draw a flow chart to show what happens to food in the gut. Start in the mouth and finish when the food passes out of the body.

absorb	**digestion**	**gut**	**anus**	**digestive enzymes**
saliva	**acid**	**small intestine**	**large intestine**	**rectum**

5.4 Gut rot

'I'm getting cramp in my muscles'

Eating or drinking too much, a **fever** and some **bacteria** can make you sick. They can also give you the runs! Sickness and **diarrhoea** is the body's way of getting rid of any 'bad' things, but it also gets rid of lots of water and salts which we need!

Muscles that are working hard need more blood than usual. After a meal lots more blood goes to the gut to absorb the digested food. The muscles cannot get the blood they need! They hurt! We call this **cramp**.

Constipation happens when the undigested food stays in the large intestine for too long. It dries out and is harder to push out of the body. Eating more **fibre** can help.

Keeping foods safe from bacteria

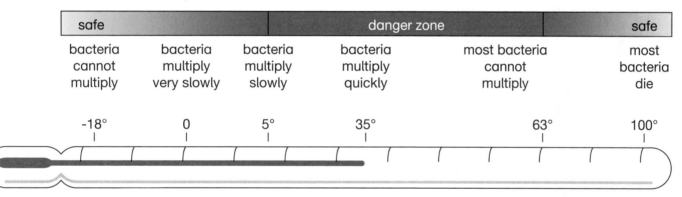

safe			danger zone		safe
bacteria cannot multiply	bacteria multiply very slowly	bacteria multiply slowly	bacteria multiply quickly	most bacteria cannot multiply	most bacteria die
-18°	0	5°	35°	63°	100°

I What could be upsetting the body builder in the cartoon above?

Look at the information given in the diagram above and answer the questions below.

2 What is the danger zone for bacteria?

3 Why is it dangerous to leave food out in a warm room?

4 How could the body builder kill the bacteria in his food?

fever   bacteria   diarrhoea   cramp   constipation fibre

6.1 Running into the ground

These people look exhausted! They have just run over 26 miles! Their muscles have been working very hard and will have produced large amounts of heat and carbon dioxide.

Your body needs energy to be able to do anything. It gets **energy** from a chemical reaction called **respiration**. Respiration uses up sugar and **oxygen** and gives out **carbon dioxide** and water. If the supply of oxygen stops for more than a few minutes your body cannot get enough energy to continue living. It dies. The body has to get rid of the carbon dioxide. Too much carbon dioxide can poison you. Your lungs swap oxygen for carbon dioxide when you breathe.

Your body keeps the levels of oxygen and carbon dioxide within certain limits. When you run faster you need more energy. This means you need more oxygen. Your body gets this by breathing more quickly.

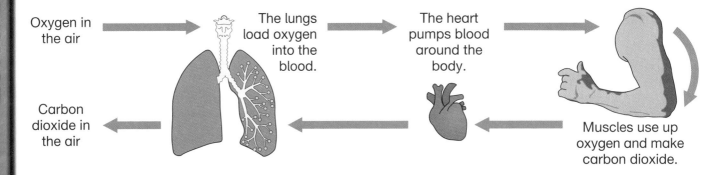

Oxygen in the air → The lungs load oxygen into the blood. → The heart pumps blood around the body. → Muscles use up oxygen and make carbon dioxide. → The heart pumps blood around the body. → Carbon dioxide in the air

1 What is respiration?
2 What chemicals does respiration make?
3 Why does the body need to carry out respiration?
4 How does the body get rid of the wastes from respiration?
5 A runner who runs very fast uses up the oxygen in his body more quickly than one who runs slowly. Why?
6 Plan an investigation to see how exercise changes the way your body breathes.

energy   respiration   oxygen   carbon dioxide

6.2 Cold enough to freeze...

That must hurt! The people in the photograph have just come out of a sauna with temperatures of 40°C and now they're jumping into a frozen lake! And that's supposed to be fun?

Hot

Blood flows to the skin's surface so it cools down in the air. You look redder.

Sweat is released. It takes heat from you when it evaporates.

Hairs lie flat so less air is trapped.

Body temperature

Cold

The blood flow to the ears and nose is reduced to cut down heat loss.

Muscles **shiver** to create heat.

Most blood keeps away from the skin to reduce heat loss. You look paler.

Hair stands on end to trap warm air.

Your body works best at 37°C. If you get too cold you could get hypothermia. **Hypothermia** makes you feel sleepy and you can pass into a very deep sleep called a **coma**. You could die. Getting too hot can also be very dangerous.

To make sure that your internal **temperature** remains at around 37°C, your body automatically reacts to changes in the temperature around it. If your surroundings are cold, your body has ways to keep itself warm. Stored **fat** and clothing also help. If your surroundings are hot, your body has ways to cool itself down. This is part of the body's control system – it balances your temperature.

1 What is a healthy body temperature?
2 What is hypothermia?
3 List the things your body does to keep you cool in hot weather.
4 List the things your body does to keep you warm in cold weather.

hypothermia	**coma**	**temperature**	**fat**	**shiver**
sweat				

6.3 Controlling water levels

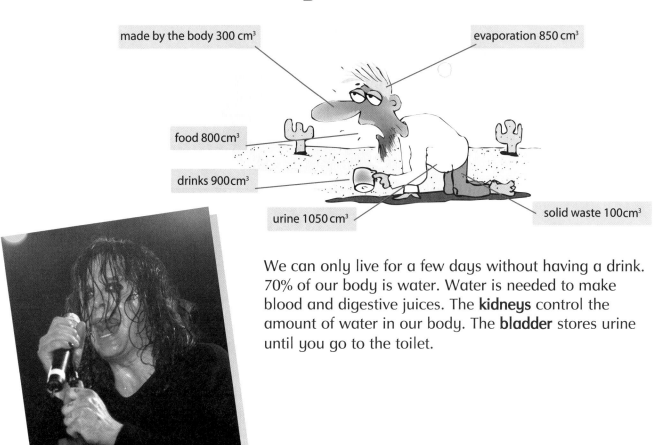

made by the body 300 cm³

evaporation 850 cm³

food 800 cm³

drinks 900 cm³

urine 1050 cm³

solid waste 100 cm³

We can only live for a few days without having a drink. 70% of our body is water. Water is needed to make blood and digestive juices. The **kidneys** control the amount of water in our body. The **bladder** stores urine until you go to the toilet.

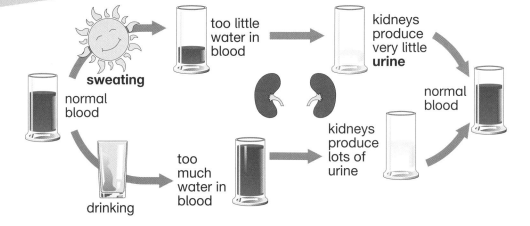

sweating

normal blood

too little water in blood

kidneys produce very little **urine**

normal blood

drinking

too much water in blood

kidneys produce lots of urine

1 Why is it important for people to drink water?
2 Which part of your body gets rid of extra water?
3 Why do you produce less urine on days when you do not have much to drink?
4 Use the drawing at the top of the page to work out how much water we take in and lose each day.

kidney   bladder   urine   sweat

6.4 Keeping sweet!

Steve Redgrave has diabetes but it didn't stop him becoming an Olympic gold medal winner four times over! However, he does need to be careful about what he eats. He also needs injections every day to control the level of sugar in his blood.

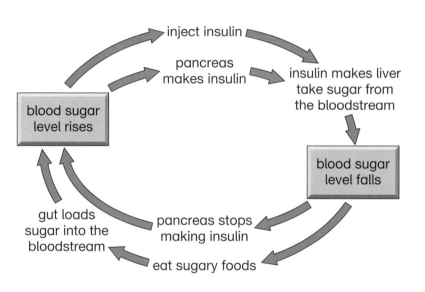

inject insulin

pancreas makes insulin

insulin makes liver take sugar from the bloodstream

blood sugar level rises

blood sugar level falls

gut loads sugar into the bloodstream

pancreas stops making insulin

eat sugary foods

A lot of the food we eat contains **sugar**. We use some sugar for energy straight away and **store** the rest for later. A chemical called **insulin** tells your body when there is spare sugar to store. People who do not make insulin have an illness called **diabetes**. They do not store extra sugar. Too much sugar stays in their blood. At other times they run out of sugar. They may feel faint, become unconscious or even go into a coma. Diabetic people need to inject themselves with insulin every day and be careful about what food they eat.

1 What do we need sugar for?
2 List three foods which contain a lot of sugar.
3 What happens to the sugar we do not need straightaway?
4 What is diabetes?
5 How can diabetes be treated?
6 What could happen to a diabetic person who does not have his or her injections?

sugar	**store**	**insulin**	**diabetes**

7.1 Tie-dyed and tasteful

Very colourful – but probably not suitable for school! Many of these fabrics started out as plain white and were coloured with dyes.

A **dye** is a substance that can change the colour of something else. Many traditional dyes come from a plant or vegetable. Onion skins can dye white cotton cloth yellow. Your jeans were probably treated with a blue dye called **indigo** which is also made from a plant. There are also many **artificial** dyes which tend to provide the bright colours in clothes. These dyes come as a powder.

Sometimes a substance is added to the dye solution to help the dye stick to the cloth. This is called a **mordant**. Here are some results obtained when cotton cloth was heated with water containing onion skins.

Temperature	Experiment 1: salt added	Experiment 2: no salt added
	Percentage of dye absorbed	Percentage of dye absorbed
60°C	15	8
80°C	20	10
100°C	25	12

1 What is a dye?
2 What do the results above tell you about the best temperature for dyeing cloth?
3 What is a mordant?
4 Is salt a mordant for the dye in onion skins? Explain your answer.
5 Plan an investigation to see which of the following would dye cloth: beetroot, grass, plain yoghurt, raspberries.

| dye | indigo | artificial | mordant |

7.2 Acid or alkali?

Many Indian foods contain a natural dye called **turmeric**. Turmeric is made from the root of a plant. Turmeric changes colour in an **acid** or in an **alkali**. A dye which changes colour when it goes from acid to alkali is called an **indicator**.

In vinegar (an acid), turmeric is orangey-yellow. In washing powder (an alkali), turmeric turns pink. You can make indicator paper by dipping filter paper in a mixture of turmeric and water and leaving it to dry. You can then use this paper to test for acids and alkalis.

	Acid	Alkali
Taste	Sour	
Litmus paper	Pink	Blue
Turmeric paper	Orangey-yellow	Pink
Universal indicator	Orange	Blue
Examples	Vinegar, lemon juice, hydrochloric acid	Washing soda, sodium hydroxide, many soaps

But solutions are not just acid or alkaline – some are very strongly acid while others are only just acid. Scientists use a scale called the **pH scale** to measure the acidity or alkalinity of a solution. The chart shows the pH for some different solutions. A special indicator called **universal indicator (UI)** is used to check for pH. UI has a different colour for every different pH value.

The pH scale

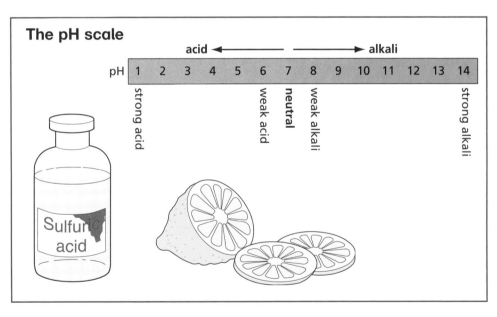

acid ← → alkali

pH | 1 | 2 | 3 | 4 | 5 | 6 | 7 | 8 | 9 | 10 | 11 | 12 | 13 | 14

strong acid · weak acid · neutral · weak alkali · strong alkali

Sulfuric acid

1　What colour does litmus paper go in an acid?
2　What colour does litmus paper go in an alkali?
3　How could you make indicator paper?
4　What is universal indicator used for?

**turmeric　acid　alkali　indicator　litmus paper
pH scale　universal indicator (UI)**

7.3 Reactions of acids

Many **acids** react in the same way. This allows us to predict what might happen when we react an acid with an unknown chemical.

Reactions with metals

Acids dissolve many metals and give off the gas **hydrogen**. Not all metals react this way, and sometimes the reaction is so slow that you can only see it after many years. A good example of a metal that reacts with an acid is **magnesium**.

Reactions with carbonates

Acids react quickly with carbonates to produce the gas **carbon dioxide**. We can see this reaction easily because the powdered carbonate fizzes as the gas is given off.

Neutralisation

When acids and alkalis react together they form a **neutral** solution. The reaction is called **neutralisation**. Neutralisation produces a solution which is not alkaline or acid. Pure water is neutral.

Testing for hydrogen

Light the gas and it will burn with a popping sound. Burning hydrogen in air produces water. Sometimes you can see these droplets of moisture on the side of a test tube or gas jar.

Testing for carbon dioxide

The gas will put out a lighted splint. It also turns limewater milky when it bubbles through it.

1. What gas is made when an acid reacts with a metal?
2. What gas is made when an acid reacts with a carbonate?
3. What two types of chemicals do you need for a neutralisation reaction?
4. A gas burns with a popping sound. What gas is it?
5. How could you test for carbon dioxide?

| acid | hydrogen | magnesium | carbon dioxide |
| neutral | neutralisation | | |

7.4 Using neutralisation

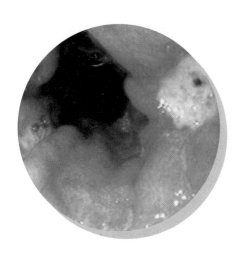

Your stomach contains about one litre of **hydrochloric acid**. This breaks down your food. Too much acid in your stomach can cause **indigestion**. Indigestion tablets contain a weak alkali called **bicarbonate of soda**. When acids and alkalis react together they form a **neutral** solution. The reaction is called **neutralisation**. The reaction removes the excess acid and the pain fades.

Too much acid can also damage plants. Most plants prefer the soil to be neutral or very slightly acidic. If the acidity of the soil is wrong plants cannot get minerals from the soil. Farmers use a neutralisation reaction to control the acidity of their soil. They add **lime** to the soil. This helps to neutralise the acid and makes it easier for plants to grow.

I What is a neutral solution? Give an example.
2 What happens when indigestion tablets are added to hydrochloric acid?
3 Plan an investigation to see which indigestion tablets are the best.
4 Why are indigestion tablets sometimes called antacids?
5 Why do farmers add lime to their soil?

**hydrochloric acid   indigestion   bicarbonate of soda
neutral   neutralisation   lime**

8.1 The best coffee shop in the world!

Who makes the best coffee? There is a huge choice from all over the world. Chemicals in the coffee **dissolve** in water to give a good hot drink. Some of the coffee will not dissolve and is left behind as the grounds. We say the grounds are **insoluble**. The drink is a **solution** of coffee flavours and colours in water. The water is called a **solvent** because it dissolves the coffee.

Solute + solvent → solution
Coffee flavours and colours + hot water → coffee drink

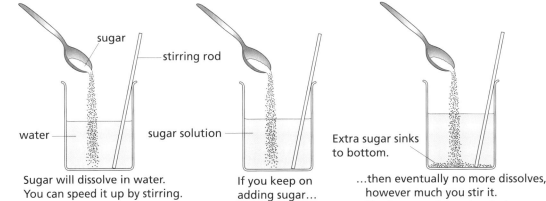

Sugar will dissolve in water. You can speed it up by stirring.

If you keep on adding sugar…

…then eventually no more dissolves, however much you stir it. You have made a saturated sugar solution.

Some people like sugar in their coffee. Sugar is a solid that is **soluble**. This means that it will dissolve in a solvent. Things that dissolve in a solvent are called **solutes**. There are three ways to help a solid dissolve more quickly:

a stir the liquid
b make the solid particles smaller
c heat the liquid

Some solutes do not dissolve in water. They are insoluble in water but they may dissolve in another solvent. Chocolate is a good example – it does not dissolve in water but does dissolve in cooking oil.

1 What is a solute? Name three.
2 What is a solvent? Name two.
3 List three ways to help a solid dissolve more quickly.
4 Plan an investigation to find out which of your answers to Question 3 has the biggest affect.
5 Write a sentence with each of the key words in it to show you know what the word means.

insoluble	solution	solvent	soluble	solute
dissolve				

8.2 Mixtures

A flapjack is a mixture of butter, syrup, oats and salt. A mixture is something that contains two or more different **substances**.

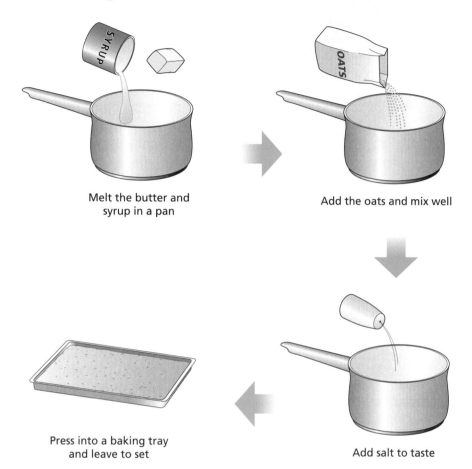

Melt the butter and syrup in a pan

Add the oats and mix well

Add salt to taste

Press into a baking tray and leave to set

Salt is a pure substance: it contains only salt. You cannot separate it into two substances. Syrup is a solution of sugar in water. You could boil off the water and be left with just sugar. So, syrup is more complicated than salt. Butter and oats are even more complicated mixtures. They contain lots of different substances.

Most of the things that we cook are mixtures. Before a cake can be cooked the **ingredients** have to be mixed together. In fact, mixtures are very common. Air is a mixture of gases. Milk is a mixture of water, salts, fats, sugars and protein. Even people are mixtures of thousands of chemicals.

1　What is the difference between a pure substance and a mixture?
2　List ten mixtures from your kitchen at home. Now try to list five pure substances.
3　Which are more common – mixtures or pure substances?
4　Is Coca Cola a mixture or a pure substance? How can you tell?

| mixture | substance | ingredients |

8.3 Too complicated for me!

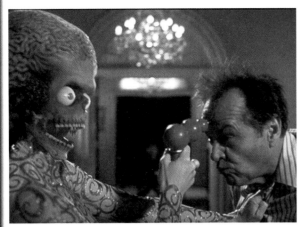

This alien is very, very clever! With a huge brain he can understand so much. For the rest of us it's a good idea to start with simple ideas first and then work up to the more complicated ideas. Scientists try to use simple ideas to explain complicated things.

Everything is made of **atoms**. There are only about one hundred different types of atom. In different combinations these atoms make up everything in the universe. The properties of a substance depend on the type of atoms it contains. The air we breathe contains **oxygen**. Oxygen contains only one type of atom. We say oxygen is an **element**. So atoms and elements are simple things.

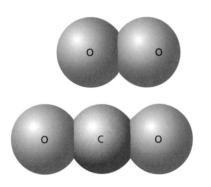

Air also contains **carbon dioxide**. Carbon dioxide contains oxygen and carbon atoms. The oxygen and carbon atoms join together to make a **compound**. Pubs put carbon dioxide into barrels of beer to make it fizz. The carbon dioxide is pure: it contains only carbon dioxide. But, we know that carbon dioxide contains two sorts of atom – carbon and oxygen. Compounds are more complicated than elements.

This **copper** bracelet contains only coppper atoms. Copper is an element.

Sugar is a pure compound. Sugar contains atoms of **hydrogen**, oxygen and carbon.

A cup of coffee is a **mixture** of compounds: it contains lots of different substances. Each of these substances has more than one type of atom. Mixtures are some of the most complicated things on the planet.

1 What is an atom?
2 About how many different types of atom are there?
3 What is an element?
4 Name two compounds.
5 What is the difference between a compound and a mixture?

| atom | oxygen | element | carbon dioxide | compound |
| copper | hydrogen | mixture | | |

8.4 The world's largest cake?

Every year São Paulo produces a birthday cake for the city on January 25th. Each year they make the cake a metre longer. So in 2003 when São Paulo was 449 years old, the cake was 449 metres long!

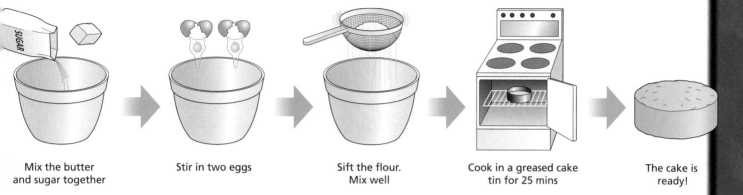

Mix the butter and sugar together

Stir in two eggs

Sift the flour. Mix well

Cook in a greased cake tin for 25 mins

The cake is ready!

Raw cake mixture is not the same as a cooked cake. When we cook the mixture it forms a new substance. This change is called a **chemical reaction**. A chemical reaction changes the starting mixture into something completely new. You cannot change the cake back to the original ingredients.

In every chemical reaction two things happen:

a a new substance forms
b the change is difficult to undo

Both of these things happen because the atoms in the mixture link up in different ways. The atoms are the same at the beginning and the end, but they are arranged in a different way.

Self-raising flour is used in many cake recipes. Self-raising flour contains baking powder. Baking powder is a chemical which gives out carbon dioxide **gas** when it gets hot. The carbon dioxide makes the cake rise. A good sponge cake is full of carbon dioxide. We can show the reaction as a word equation:

baking powder → carbon dioxide and sodium carbonate

Some drinks contain carbon dioxide. The gas bubbles are dissolved in the drink and when they rise up they make the drink fizzy. When they have all risen to the surface the drink tastes flat – it is not fizzy any more.

1 What two things happen when a chemical reaction takes place?
2 Why do these happen?
3 List examples of chemical reactions that occur in your kitchen.
4 Plan an investigation to find out which brand of baking powder is best.

chemical reaction   gas

35

9.1 Messy work!

This will take a while to clean up! This is because these paints do not dissolve in water. Unfortunately, the strong **solvents** that can dissolve them also damage the skin.

Choosing a solvent is not always easy. The table below shows some solvents and the **solutes** they can dissolve. One solvent cannot dissolve everything. Many solvents are powerful chemicals that can be dangerous.

Stain	Solvent	Dangers
Gloss paint	White spirit Turps	Burns very easily
Nail varnish	Nail varnish remover	
Waxes and grease	Trichloroethane Paraffin Meths	**Toxic** fumes
Crude oil	White spirit Some powerful detergents	Can dissolve the oils that protect the skin

1 Why do people have to be careful when they use trichloroethane indoors?
2 Which solvent could I use to clean gloss paint from paintbrushes?
3 People warm water to help it to dissolve salt more easily. Why is this a very dangerous thing to do with meths?
4 Plan an investigation to find out which solvent will clean ink from white cloth.

solvent   solute   toxic

9.2 Soaps and detergents

When one of the authors of this book was three years old, he climbed up the chimney in his house to look for Father Christmas! His mum came in to see two little boots dangling in the fireplace! She pulled him out and had to dunk him in a bath with washing-up liquid to clean him up!

Cleaning children and their clothes is not always easy. Mud and dirt just seem to stick to them! If you tried to dissolve the dirt and wash it away with water it would take a very long time! You need **soap** for the children and a **detergent** for their clothes.

Soaps are made from animal fats or plant oils heated with an alkali called sodium hydroxide. Soaps are expensive to make and can form **scum** with some types of water. You might have seen scum as a sticky white ring around the bowl or bath. Detergents are cheaper to make than soaps and they do not form scum. They are made from chemicals produced from **crude oil**.

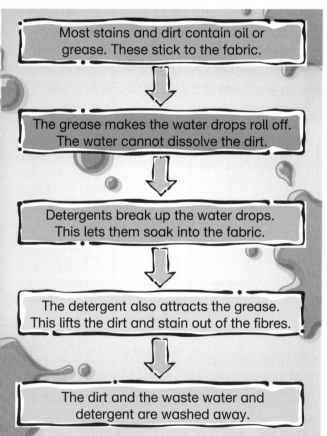

Most stains and dirt contain oil or grease. These stick to the fabric.

⬇

The grease makes the water drops roll off. The water cannot dissolve the dirt.

⬇

Detergents break up the water drops. This lets them soak into the fabric.

⬇

The detergent also attracts the grease. This lifts the dirt and stain out of the fibres.

⬇

The dirt and the waste water and detergent are washed away.

Soap powder	Stain	Temperature /°C	Time needed /mins
Scotto	Blackcurrant juice	40	30
Scotto	Blackcurrant juice	50	20
Scotto	Blackcurrant juice	60	10

1 Give two differences between soap and detergents.
2 Explain how detergents work.
3 Draw a bar chart to show the time needed to clean blackcurrant juice using Scotto at different temperatures.
4 Why don't we always boil clothes when we wash them to make sure they are clean?

soap   **detergent**   **scum**   **crude oil**

9.3 Enzymes and soaps

A bit of a messy eater? Some of those foods will **stain**! Ordinary detergents will not work at low temperatures. You could clean the stains with very hot water but this would spoil the clothes. Some washing powders contain chemicals called **enzymes**. Enzymes can digest food stains in the same way that they digest the foods that you eat. Washing powders with enzymes are often called **biological** powders.

Some washing powders also contain **bleach**. Bleach reacts with coloured chemicals and makes them go white. This means that any stains are more difficult to see. Unfortunately, bleach also makes colours fade. Powders with bleach are only used to clean white clothes or fabrics.

Delicate fabrics like wool or silk need a gentle cleaner. Soap flakes or liquid soaps are better for these fabrics. Not all fabrics can be cleaned at the same temperature. The white cotton T-shirt needs a hot wash. The red jumper is not **colour fast**. This means that its colour may come out in the wash. What would happen if the jumper and the T-shirt were washed together?

1 What special chemicals do biological detergents contain?
2 Design the outside of a detergent packet. You will need to decide what type of detergent it will contain. What information will you need to put on it?
3 Sort these clothes into four groups for washing: silk shirt, tea towel, blue jeans, baby's bib, pure wool sweater, cotton shirt with oil on, patterned sheet, dish cloth, tablecloth, white towel, baby's vest, football kit.

Gentle soap flakes	Normal detergent	Biological detergent	Powder with bleach

stain   **enzyme**   **biological**   **bleach**   **colour fast**

9.4 Filthy scum!

We use soaps in the bath, not detergents. This means we often get a tidemark around the bath when the water drains away. This mark is made of **scum**. It forms when soaps react with chemicals dissolved in the tap water.

Hard water contains lots of dissolved substances and so produces a lot of scum. It is difficult to make hard water lather. **Soft water** contains less dissolved substances. It produces very little scum and needs very little soap to produce a good lather. Hard water is good for one thing – beer tastes better made with hard water. All the best breweries are based in areas with hard water supplies.

There are two ways to remove scum.

Abrasive cleaners
These are usually powders or creams that contain small bits of grit which scratch the scum off the surface of the bath. Abrasive cleaners are suitable for china and porcelain.

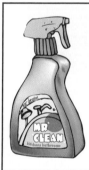

Non-abrasive cleaners
These contain solvents that dissolve the grease in the scum. They are usually sold as creams or liquids. They are more expensive than the abrasive cleaners but they do not scratch soft surfaces. They are used to clean plastic and glass.

In hard water areas **limescale** forms on taps and baths. Limescale is made up of white crystals left behind when water evaporates. Sometimes the crystals can be light green or brown. You can use non-abrasive cleaners to get rid of limescale. Acids in the cleaners react with the crystals to dissolve them away.

1　Explain the difference between hard and soft water.
2　What does abrasive mean?
3　How does a non-abrasive cream clean scum from a bath?
4　Why is it a bad idea to use an abrasive cleaner on a plastic bath?
5　What causes limescale?

scum	hard water	soft water	abrasive
non-abrasive	limescale		

10.1 Golden oldie

Gold does not react easily with other chemicals. This is why the mask in the photograph still looks so good. When a metal **reacts** with the air it changes into a new chemical. Scientists say it has **corroded**. Rusty **iron** is a good example of this. We try to prevent things made of iron from reacting with the air by painting them. This keeps the air away from the surface of the metal.

Gold was used in the earliest times, long before bronze or iron. You can find tiny specks of pure gold in the rivers and streams of North Wales. Because gold is so heavy it settles at the bottom of rivers and streams. Some people pan for gold by swirling the stones and grit from the river bed in a plate. The small particles of gold sparkle in the light and can be collected – if you're lucky!

Gold is a precious metal. In 2003, one gramme of gold cost roughly £20. That's a speck of gold that is roughly the same size as a grain of sand! At the same time, all of the iron in a car engine costs less than £25.

But gold is just like any other metal in other ways. It is shiny and can be beaten into flat sheets. Heat and electricity pass easily through both gold and iron.

1 Write a sentence with the word corrode in it.
2 List four things that are true about both gold and iron.
3 Give two differences between gold and iron.
4 How would you recognise tiny fragments of gold in river gravel?

gold	react	corrode	iron

10.2 Suits you, sir!

Gold is still used for jewellery. Pure gold jewellery is soft and very expensive. Jewellers often mix gold with other metals like **nickel** or **silver** to make a harder, cheaper alloy. An **alloy** is a mixture of two pure metals.

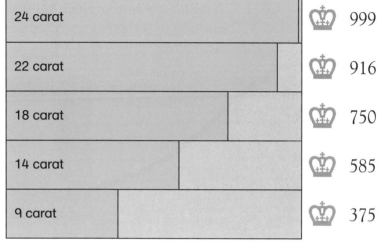

24 carat		999
22 carat		916
18 carat		750
14 carat		585
9 carat		375

Amount of gold in 1000 g of the alloy   Hallmark

But how could you test a gold-coloured substance to see if it really is pure gold? Use some of the clues here to plan a test:

People would try to bite a gold coin – if it was soft enough to dent, it was pure gold.

Gold is easy to hammer into flat sheets called **gold leaf**. Other metals are more difficult to flatten in this way.

Gold is a very heavy metal.

Acid reacts with many metals – but not gold.

1   What is an alloy?
2   Why is an alloy sometimes better for jewellery than pure gold?
3   Why is an 18 carat gold ring cheaper than a 24 carat ring?
4   Why do people prefer to buy jewellery made of gold, silver or **platinum** rather than iron, zinc or brass?
5   Plan a test to discover if a gold-coloured substance brought into the laboratory is pure gold or not.

nickel	**silver**	**alloy**	**gold leaf**	**platinum**

10.3 Pure or plated?

Silver is much cheaper than gold – but more expensive than metals like steel. Manufacturers try to make cheap jewellery look expensive. They coat the jewellery with precious metals like silver, gold or platinum.

There are two ways to coat jewellery. Dip the piece in molten gold, silver or platinum, pull it out and let a layer of precious metal solidify onto the cheap metal jewellery. This gives a thick, uneven **coating** of precious metal.

A better method is **electroplating**. Electroplating produces a thin, even coating of the precious metal. Electroplating is also used to coat cutlery with silver.

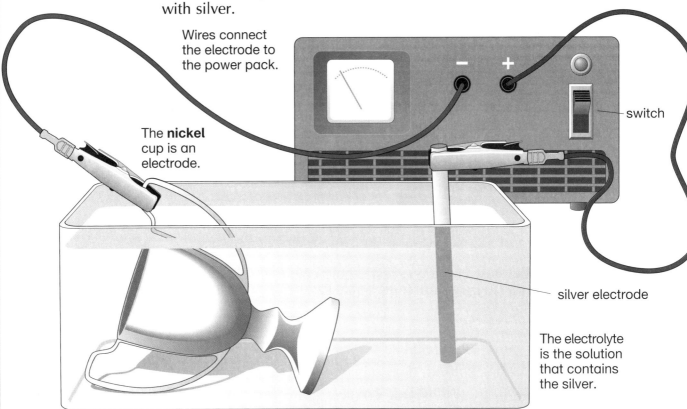

Wires connect the electrode to the power pack.

switch

The **nickel** cup is an electrode.

silver electrode

The electrolyte is the solution that contains the silver.

Electrolysis can also be used to **purify** metals like copper. If you use a positive electrode of impure copper it will slowly dissolve away. However, the copper that sticks to the negative electrode is pure. This is because impurities and other metals in the solution are not attracted to the electrode.

1   Give two ways to coat a metal ring with gold.
2   What is an electrode?
3   Is the nickel cup above the positive or negative electrode?
4   What is the electrolyte in this experiment?
5   What might affect the thickness of silver on the cup?
6   Why is a thin, even coating of precious metal better than a thick, uneven coating?

| coating | electroplating | nickel | electrolysis | purify |

10.4 Displacement reactions

Chemicals containing **silver** react to light. This makes silver compounds very useful in photographs. A black and white photograph is a pattern of silver grains spread across a white paper background. Laboratories which develop films produce large amounts of waste silver. This silver is dissolved in the waste solution left over after developing the film. Silver is expensive so laboratories try to get the silver back from these solutions.

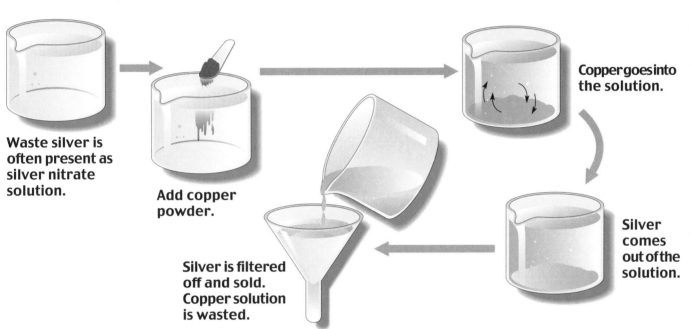

Waste silver is often present as silver nitrate solution.

Add copper powder.

Copper goes into the solution.

Silver comes out of the solution.

Silver is filtered off and sold. Copper solution is wasted.

This is an example of a **displacement reaction**. The **copper** displaces the silver from the solution. You can tell if a metal will displace silver from a solution by looking at its **reactivity**. Reactivity is a measure of how easily a metal reacts with other chemicals. A metal that is more reactive than silver will displace it from a solution.

1 Why is silver used in photographic film?
2 What does reactive mean?
3 What is a displacement reaction?
4 Why don't the laboratories worry so much about wasting copper?
5 Plan an investigation to find out which metals can displace copper from a waste solution.

| silver | displacement reaction | reactivity | copper |

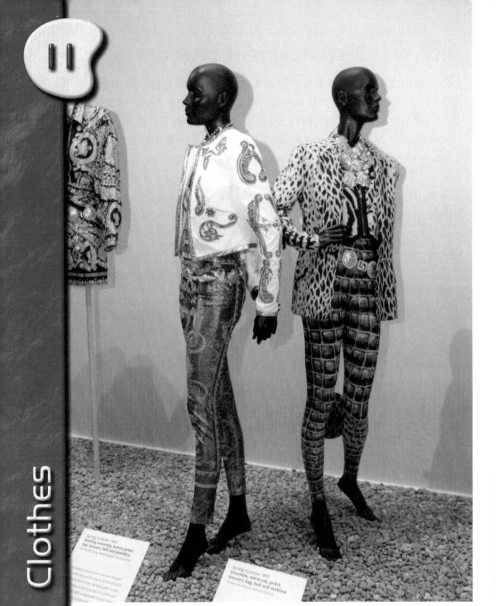

11.1 Worth millions!

These clothes are made from different **fabrics**. Some of the fabrics are made from **threads** woven together. Some have metal threads woven into them or jewels sewn onto them to make them sparkle and look more glamorous.

A fabric is a flat sheet. In the past, these sheets were made of threads woven together. Nowadays we can produce flat plastic or even rubber sheets.

In woven fabrics, the properties of the fabric depend on the thread used to make them. These threads are made of even thinner **fibres** twisted together. There are two sorts of fibre: **natural** and **artificial**.

Natural	Artificial
Silk, wool, mohair, cotton, linen	Acrylic, lycra, polyester

Fibre	Properties
Acrylic	Strong, soft and warm
Lycra	Very stretchy, springs back into shape
Nylon	Stretchy, strong, tough
Polyester	Quick drying, tough, blends well with other fibres
Wool	Stretchy, soft, warm
Cotton	Stretchy, can be cool or warm, absorbs water

1 What is a fabric?
2 What are the two sorts of fibre?
3 Which fibres would be useful for a T-shirt or vest? Why?
4 Which fibres would be useful for waterproof leggings? Why?
5 What is the biggest disadvantage of wool? Explain your answer.
6 Plan an investigation to find the strength of a thread.

| fabric | thread | fibre | natural | artificial |

11.2 Keeping it safe

Mountaineers need clothes that can cope with the toughest conditions. A waterproof and windproof jacket could save your life on a mountain. Some jackets are made from a special 'breathing' fabric. This keeps water out but lets sweat pass from your body to the outside.

Sometimes the way the fabric is made makes it very expensive. The weave affects the way the fabric behaves when it is used. Tight weaves tend to be **waterproof** and **windproof**. Open weaves stretch easily and can trap air layers which help to keep people warm. Different **yarns** cost different amounts of money. Sometimes people are willing to pay more for a designer label or a different colour.

A student weighed a beaker with fabric fixed on the top.

She poured 10 ml of water slowly over the fabric. Some of the water went through into the beaker.

She weighed the beaker and the wet fabric. Then she repeated the experiment with four different fabrics.

Fabric	Dry fabric + beaker /g	Wet fabric + beaker /g	Weight of water /g
Cotton	95	102	7
Waxed cotton	93	95	2
Nylon	90	94	4
Silicone nylon	98	99	1
Rubber	94	94	0

1 Draw a bar chart of the weight of water against the fabric.
2 Why do you think 10 ml of water was used for each fabric?
3 Which fabric is completely waterproof?
4 Which fabrics are only **water-resistant**?

> **waterproof**   **windproof**   **yarn**   **water-resistant**

11.3 Surviving fires

Firefighters depend on their clothes to save their lives. The fabrics reflect heat. They are treated with special chemicals so that they do not burn easily. Even so, fighting fires is a dangerous and difficult job.

All fabrics burn if they become hot enough. However, we can make it more difficult for them to catch fire. Some chemicals seem to reduce the chance of a fabric catching fire. We call fabrics that have been treated with these chemicals **flameproof**.

A student tested some fabrics to see how they burned before and after flameproofing. He used three equal pieces from each fabric and treated them with flameproofing chemicals.

He heated the fabrics with a bunsen burner. He timed how long before each fabric caught fire.

untreated

treated with **alum**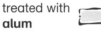

treated with **borax**

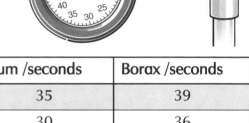

Fabric	Untreated /seconds	Alum /seconds	Borax /seconds
Cotton	30	35	39
Nylon	23	30	36
Wool	25	32	37

1 List the ways that firefighters' clothes protect them.
2 What does flameproof mean?
3 Which fabric would be most suitable for making a flameproof coat? Why?
4 Which treatment would you use?
5 Firefighters' uniforms need to be washed regularly. How might this affect their flameproof coating?
6 Plan an investigation to check your answer to Question 3.

flameproof　　**alum**　　**borax**

11.4 Footwear

Hill walkers need sensible footwear for their trip. Some people want walking boots to protect their ankles. They must be strong, comfortable and have soles with a good grip. Other people prefer comfortable, lightweight trainers with **non-slip** soles.

When manufacturers design new footwear they think about the way the shoes will be used. This helps them to decide what to make the footwear from. The **properties** of the material used to make each part of the shoe must be right or the shoe will break.

Trainer

eyeholes – must not tear when the laces are pulled tight. They can be strengthened with metal rings or extra layers of fabric or leather.

waterproof uppers – often made from fabric or leather.

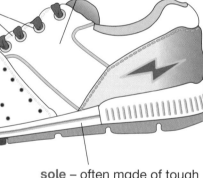

read – designed to be long-lasting and to give good grip.

sole – often made of tough spongey plastic or rubber. Some trainers have pockets of air sealed into the soles to act as shock absorbers.

Walking boot

laces – usually very long so that the boot can be tied on tightly around the foot and ankle.

tongue – is fixed to the outside of the boot on each side so that no water can get through to the person's feet.

uppers – must be waterproof. Sometimes the uppers have special one-way material patches which let sweat out from the shoe but keep water outside.

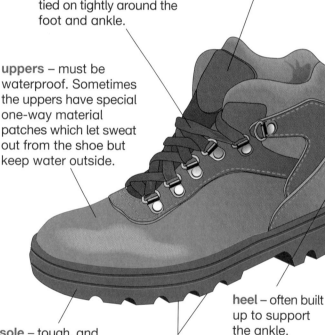

sole – tough, and also soft and spongey to absorb shocks.

tread – usually a deep tread to give a grip on slippery surfaces.

heel – often built up to support the ankle.

1 What are the soles of the trainer and walking boot made from? Why?
2 List the materials used to make the uppers of the trainer.
3 What properties must the sole of a shoe have?
4 List the different parts of a walking boot. Suggest a material you could use to make each part. Give a reason for each of your choices.
5 Plan an investigation to find out how well a piece of leather can stand up to scratches.

non-slip   properties

12.1 Hard beds

This hotel is made entirely of ice! It only survives for the winter because in the summer it melts away to become a lake!

Ice is a **solid**. It is a different physical **state** to **liquid** water but it is the same chemical. Clouds are another physical state of water. This time it is a **gas**: steam. Solids have a fixed shape, liquids can flow and gases fill all of the available space.

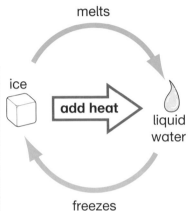

melts

ice

add heat

liquid water

freezes

The temperature at which a solid **melts** is called its **melting point.** The melting point of pure substances is fixed.

Substance	Melting point/ °C
Tungsten (used in light bulb filaments)	3400
Iron	1540
Gold	1064
Silver	960
Table salt (sodium chloride)	801
Lead	327
Ice	0
Mercury (used in some thermometers)	-39
Oxygen (gas at room temperature)	-218

1 What does the word melt mean?
2 How can we make something melt?
3 Which substance in the table has the highest melting point?
4 Which substance in the table melts at the lowest temperature?
5 Plan an investigation to find out how quickly an ice cube melts in cold and warm water.

solid	state	liquid	gas	melt	melting point

Freezing and boiling

12.2 Damp in parts

There's no problem with water freezing in pipes. But look what happens when the ice thaws! When water **freezes** the ice **expands** – it takes up more room than the water did. The pipes split and when the ice thaws again the water leaks out of the broken pipes.

Liquid water runs through the pipe.

The water freezes and expands, causing the pipe to split.

The ice melts and the water leaks through the split in the pipe.

melts

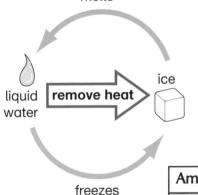

freezes

Antifreeze contains a chemical called ethylene glycol. Ethylene glycol does not freeze until the temperature drops to –16°C. **De-icer** sprays use a chemical called methanol. Methanol does not freeze until the temperature gets as low as –98°C. The temperature at which a chemical or gas freezes is called its **freezing point**.

A company wants to increase the amount of fruit juice in their ice lollies to make them taste better. They run some tests with water and orange juice. More concentrated solutions need lower temperatures to be able to freeze. The results are shown below.

Amount of juice added to water	Temperature the juice froze at
0% juice (all water)	0°C
50% juice (50% water)	–5°C
75% juice (25% water)	–10°C
100% juice (no water)	?

1 What do we mean when we say something freezes?
2 What temperature does water freeze at?
3 What pattern can you see in the above results?
4 What temperature do you think pure orange juice might freeze at? Explain your answer.

freeze	expand	antifreeze	de-icer	freezing point

12.3 Protecting your engine

Oil in car engines helps the moving parts to slide over each other more easily. This reduces the **friction** and so keeps them from wearing out. The oil **lubricates** the engine.

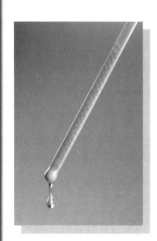

Cold oil is quite thick and takes a long time to coat all of the moving parts of an engine. Hot oil can be so thin that it runs off the parts too quickly. This means the parts are not protected. We call the runniness of liquids their **viscosity**. Thick liquids like honey have a high viscosity. Runny liquids like water have a low viscosity. Oil companies test their oils so that they have the best viscosity – not too thick when cold and not too runny when hot.

The oil is warmed to a set **temperature** and the time it takes to flow down the tube is recorded.

Use the data below to draw a line graph. Put time on the vertical axis and temperature on the horizontal axis.

Temperature /°C	Time to flow through tube /seconds
15	60
25	40
35	25
45	16
55	12

1 What does viscosity mean?
2 Why is oil used in car engines?
3 What is the problem with thick cold oil?
4 Does the time taken for the liquid to flow increase or decrease as it warms up?
5 Use your graph to find the time it would take the oil to flow down the tube at 30°C.

friction   **lubricate**   **viscosity**   **temperature**

12.4 Steamy windows!

There is water in the form of a gas in the air. We call it **water vapour.** We can't see it. It is only when we cool the air down that we can see droplets of liquid water – and that steams up the windows! Steamy windows don't have steam on them at all – it's tiny droplets of liquid water.

When gases get very cold they change state and turn into a liquid. The gases **condense** to make a liquid.

Liquids can change state to a gas or vapour. A good example is a puddle in the road drying out. This is called **evaporation**. We can heat the liquid to speed up evaporation. You know that the Sun shining on the road dries out the puddle more quickly. The rate of evaporation is also increased by air movement, which is why clothes are moved around in a tumble dryer!

When a liquid changes state and becomes a gas or vapour we say it is boiling. The temperature at which a liquid boils is called its **boiling point.** For pure substances this boiling point is fixed.

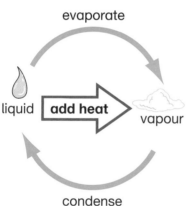

evaporate

liquid | add heat ➡ vapour

condense

Substance	Boiling point /°C
Pure water	100
Methylated spirit	80
Gold	3080

When a solid becomes a liquid, or a liquid becomes a solid or a gas, no material is lost – it is all there, just in a different state.

1 What happens when we cool a gas or vapour?
2 What do we mean by evaporation?
3 How can you speed up the evaporation of liquids?
4 What is the boiling point of pure water?
5 Plan an investigation to find the best temperature for a tumble dryer. Remember that its job is to take away water vapour without melting or damaging your clothes.

water vapour **condense** **evaporation** **boiling point**

13.1 Blackout!

On August 15th 2003 more than 50 million people were affected by the greatest power blackout in US history. For over 12 hours there was no power in many parts of the United States and Canada. Lifts, cash points, traffic lights, hotel doors and airports did not function – they relied on electricity. This all happened because one power station in Canada broke down!

Electricity needs a power supply and a complete **circuit** to flow. If the power fails or if there are any gaps in the circuit, the flow stops. If a **bulb** is shining or an electrical motor is running, we know that electricity is flowing through the circuit. A **switch** is used to control the flow of electricity by opening and closing gaps in a circuit.

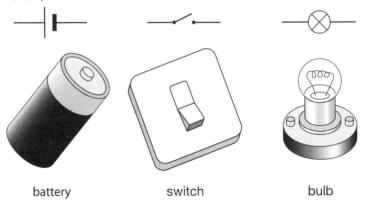

battery   switch   bulb

1   Make a list of six things in your home that use electricity.
2   For each item in your list, suggest what you would have used instead before the days of electricity.
3   Draw a picture to show how you would use a battery, switch and bulb to create a circuit where you could switch the bulb on and off.
4   Draw a circuit diagram of your circuit. Make sure you use the correct **symbols.**

| electricity | circuit | bulb | switch | battery | symbol |

Lighting up

13.2 Conductors and insulators

Electricity can be very dangerous. Each year thousands of people are killed from electric shocks, both in the home and at work. When working with electricity you need to be safe at all times. For instance, never mix water and electricity when you are working in the laboratory. You might receive a shock which could kill you.

So that we can use electricity safely, we have to be able to control where it goes. **Insulators** stop electricity from flowing and **conductors** let electricity through. We use insulators and conductors to control the flow of electricity.

The wires on a **pylon** do not have insulation. Air is an insulator, so electricity cannot pass from the wires through the air to the ground. Metals are very good conductors. On the pylon, special glass or pottery disks keep the metal wires away from the metal pylon. These disks are called insulators.

1 What is a conductor?
2 What is an insulator?
3 List three things in the classroom that conduct electricity.
4 List three things in the classroom that are electrical insulators.

insulator　　conductor　　pylon

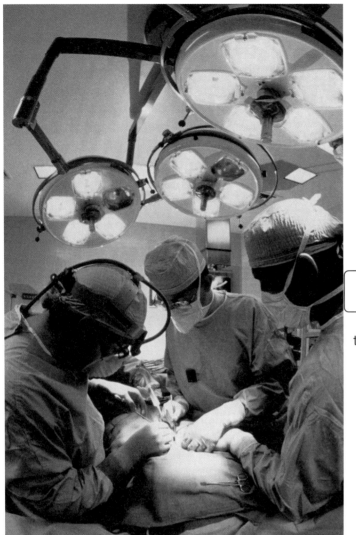

13.3 Bright lights

Electricity is used in the home, at school and at work to give us light. If a lighting circuit fails at home it doesn't really matter, but can you imagine how dangerous it would be if the circuit failed in this operating theatre?

When electricity has only one path around a circuit, it is called a **series circuit**.

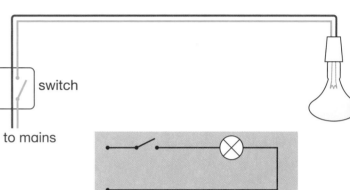

When electricity has more than one path around a circuit, it is called a **parallel circuit**. Parallel circuits can deliver more electricity, more quickly to the components in the circuit than series circuits. This means that the bulbs in the diagram can be brighter. Also, even if there is a break in one part of the parallel circuit, electricity may still be able to flow along another path in the circuit.

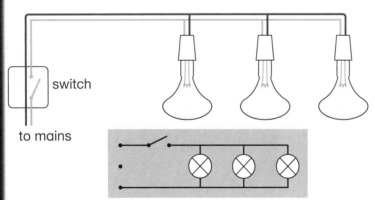

1 What is a series circuit?
2 What is a parallel circuit?
3 Give two reasons why you would use a parallel circuit to light an operating theatre.

series circuit   parallel circuit

13.4 We've got the power

There are hundreds of switches on the control board in this power station. They control the flow of electricity through the power station as well as controlling the flow of electricity to thousands of homes, schools and businesses. After the 1999 solar eclipse when people returned to their desks at work and switched on kettles at home, there was a massive increase in power needed from power stations all over the country. Power station managers were prepared for this and had allowed more power into the system.

Switches control whether electricity flows or not. The wires in a circuit allow the electricity to flow through the circuit. The amount of electricity flowing through a circuit is called the **current**. An **ammeter** is used to measure current. The more electricity that flows through a circuit, the larger the reading on the ammeter. An ammeter gives the reading in **amps**.

Wires slightly **resist** the flow of current. Insulators resist it so well that no electricity flows at all.

Dimmer switches control the resistance in a circuit. A light will shine more brightly if the resistance is low.

The central plastic knob can turn the metal contact underneath. The electricity flows through the resistor into the middle contact and then to the light bulb.

plastic insulating case

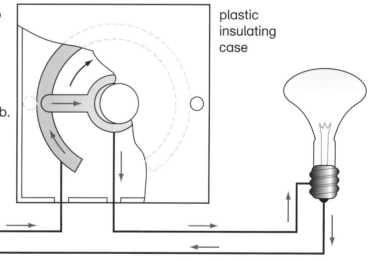

to mains

1 Why do power stations need to control how much electricity is flowing out of the power station?
2 What happens to the brightness of a bulb when the current is bigger?
3 What does an ammeter measure?
4 What is a dimmer switch?

| current | ammeter | amp | resist | dimmer |

14.1 Batteries

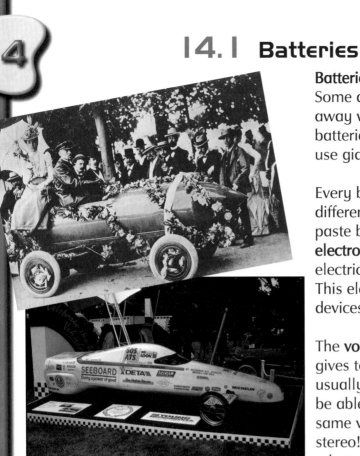

Batteries come in lots of different shapes and sizes. Some are **rechargeable** and others must be thrown away when they have been used. Different types of batteries are used for different jobs. These electric cars use giant batteries that weigh more than their engines!

Every battery has two **terminals**, each of which is a different metal. Inside the battery there is a liquid or paste between the terminals. This is called the **electrolyte**. **Chemical reactions** inside the battery make electricity flow along a wire connected to the terminals. This electricity is used to power all sorts of electrical devices.

The **voltage** of a battery is the amount of energy it gives to the electricity created inside it. Batteries usually have the voltage written on them. You wouldn't be able to drive an electric car with a battery of the same voltage as the one you use in your personal stereo! You can use a **voltmeter** to check the voltage of a battery.

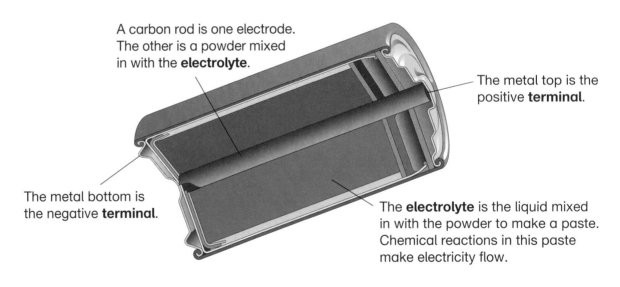

A carbon rod is one electrode. The other is a powder mixed in with the **electrolyte**.

The metal top is the positive **terminal**.

The metal bottom is the negative **terminal**.

The **electrolyte** is the liquid mixed in with the powder to make a paste. Chemical reactions in this paste make electricity flow.

1 What is a battery?
2 Name three things you or your family own that contain batteries.
3 How would you find out the voltage of a battery that was not labelled?
4 Why do different battery operated devices need batteries of different voltages?

**battery   rechargeable   terminal   electrolyte
chemical reaction   voltage   voltmeter**

Power

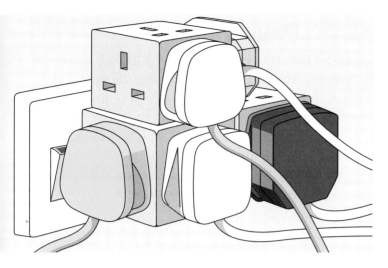

14.2 Three-pin plugs

Batteries are fine for things that we need to carry around with us, but for bigger items like televisions and stereos, you're better off getting electricity from the **mains supply**.

You need to be careful when using electricity at home. Look at the set of plugs on the left – what do you think is dangerous here? Do you think that the person who has done this has enough **sockets** in their house?

The **plug** in the drawing below is designed so that it is safe to use. The electricity flows along two wires, called **live** and **neutral**. The third wire, called the **earth** wire, is there for safety. Electricity only flows along the earth wire when something has gone wrong with the circuit. Not all plugs have an earth wire – only items with metal parts need one.

It is really important that the correct **current** passes through electrical equipment. If the current is too large, the equipment may be damaged. To avoid this, we put **fuses** into plugs. A fuse contains a thin piece of wire which melts if too much current passes through it. This breaks the circuit and stops the flow of electricity. The most common types of fuse are 1 amp, 3 amp and 13 amp.

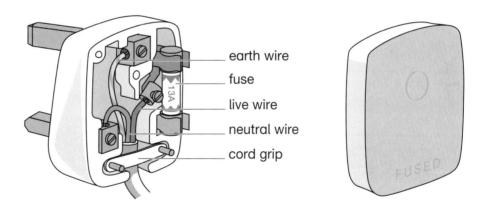

earth wire
fuse
live wire
neutral wire
cord grip

1 Which parts of the plug are metal so that electricity can flow through them?
2 Which parts are plastic so that electricity can't flow through them?
3 What is the fuse for?
4 Draw and label a diagram of a three-pin plug. Be careful to make the wires the right colours.

| mains supply | socket | plug | live | neutral |
| earth | current | fuse | | |

14.3 Paying the bills

Electricity costs money. The more you use, the more you pay for. An **electricity meter** records how much electricity has been used. The meter lets the electricity company work out how much the electricity bill should be. Electricity is sold in **units**. One unit of electricity is enough to listen to your stereo for ten hours, watch television for eight hours or run a single bar electric fire for one hour. Appliances that give out heat tend to use more electricity.

We can work out how much electricity something uses by looking at its **power** rating. Powerful appliances use a lot of electricity. Power is measured in **watts** (using the symbol W).

To understand an electricity bill, we need to know how many units have been used. This is done by subtracting the value of the previous meter reading from the current meter reading. This figure is then multiplied by the price per unit of electricity to find out how much the electricity used will cost. A fixed charge is then added on to find out the total amount owed to the electricity company.

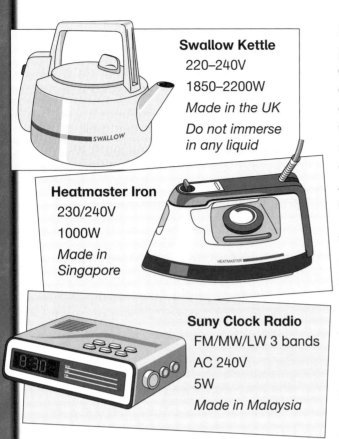

Swallow Kettle
220–240V
1850–2200W
Made in the UK
Do not immerse in any liquid

Heatmaster Iron
230/240V
1000W
Made in Singapore

Suny Clock Radio
FM/MW/LW 3 bands
AC 240V
5W
Made in Malaysia

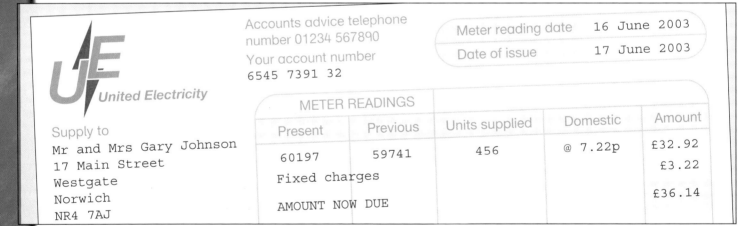

Accounts advice telephone number 01234 567890
Your account number
6545 7391 32

United Electricity

Supply to
Mr and Mrs Gary Johnson
17 Main Street
Westgate
Norwich
NR4 7AJ

Meter reading date	16 June 2003
Date of issue	17 June 2003

METER READINGS				
Present	Previous	Units supplied	Domestic	Amount
60197	59741	456	@ 7.22p	£32.92
Fixed charges				£3.22
AMOUNT NOW DUE				£36.14

1 What is power measured in?
2 How long have you watched television for if you use up two units of electricity?
3 Looking at the electricity bill, how many units of electricity have been used?
4 How much does each unit cost?
5 How much is the bill in total?

electricity meter   **unit**   **power**   **watts**

15.1 Attracting and repelling

Magnets are made of iron or steel. Things which stick to magnets are called magnetic. Only three pure metals are magnetic: iron, nickel and cobalt. Steel is magnetic because it contains iron. The magnetic tape in cassettes contains tiny bits of iron stuck in a plastic ribbon.

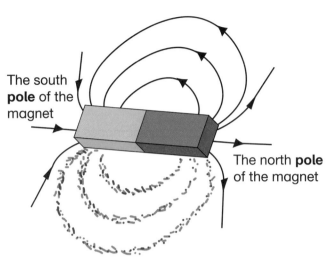

The south pole of the magnet

The north pole of the magnet

Magnetic forces pull iron filings towards the field lines.

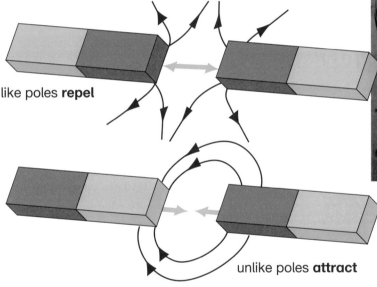

like poles repel

unlike poles attract

WILLOWGARTH HIGH SCHOOL
BRIERLEY ROAD
GRIMETHORPE
BARNSLEY S72 7AJ
TEL: (01226) 711542 FAX: (01226) 711560

1 How many magnetic materials are there in your classroom?
2 What are the two poles of a magnet called?
3 If you put the north poles of two magnets together, what happens?
4 What happens when you put the north pole of one magnet next to the south pole of another magnet?

| magnet | magnetic | pole | magnetic force | repel |
| attract |

Magnets

59

15.2 Where am I?

Have you ever been to a new place and got lost? It's hard to find your way when you don't know where you're going! Imagine being in the desert with no sign posts and no-one to ask for directions – you would need a map and a **compass** to help you to find your way.

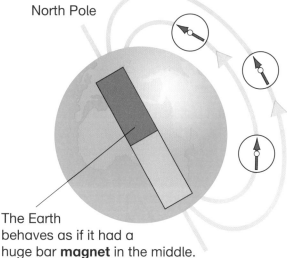

The compass needle points to the Earth's North Pole.

North Pole

The Earth behaves as if it had a huge bar **magnet** in the middle.

South Pole

All the compass points are marked so you can find out which way you are facing.

The needle can spin round.

The needle is a small magnet. The arrowhead always points north.

1 Which of the Earth's poles does the compass needle point towards?
2 Find out whether you live in the north, south, east or west of your town or village.
3 Which direction is your school from your house?

compass   magnet

15.3 Big magnets!

Scrap yards contain tonnes of metal. Moving it around could be a hard job. However, with an **electromagnet** it's easy – just switch on the magnet and lift!

You cannot switch an ordinary magnet on and off. It always pulls with the same **strength**. If you wrap insulated wire around a piece of metal, you can make a magnet that you can turn on and off. When electricity flows through the wire, the metal becomes a strong magnet. When the electricity stops, the metal is only a weak magnet.

A power pack supplies the electromagnet with electricity. When the electricity is on, a **magnetic field** forms. The nail and **coil** behave like a bar magnet.

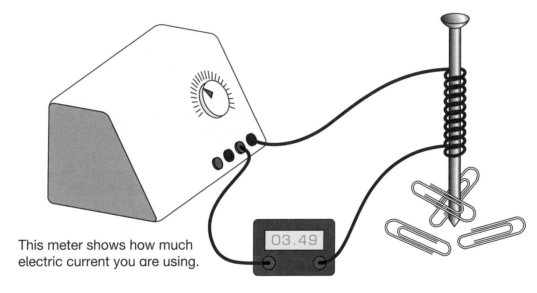

This meter shows how much electric current you are using.

`03.49`

1 What is the main difference between an electromagnet and an ordinary magnet?
2 How do you think electromagnets got their name?
3 List three things electromagnets can be used for.
4 What happens to an electromagnet when you switch off the electricity?
5 How can you make an electromagnet stronger?

| **electromagnet** | **strength** | **magnetic field** | **coil** |

15.4 Make some noise

Glastonbury is one of the biggest rock festivals in the world. Giant speakers are used to make sure that every one of the tens of thousands of spectators can hear the music. The speakers are in large towers on either side of the stage.

Loudspeakers use **electromagnets** to work. The electromagnet makes a cone of paper **vibrate**, which produces sounds in the air.

The cassette player sends electrical signals to the coil. Signals switch the electromagnet on and off. The large permanent magnet helps to push and pull on the small coil.

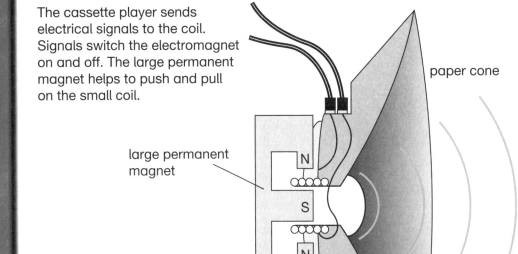

paper cone

large permanent magnet

The coil makes the cone of the loudspeaker vibrate. This cone makes sounds in the air.

1 List five things which use a loudspeaker.
2 How does the electrical signal get into the loudspeaker?
3 Which bit of the loudspeaker makes the sound?
4 What happens to the cone when the coil becomes a magnet?
5 What happens to the coil when the signal reaches the speaker?

| loudspeaker | electromagnet | vibrate |

16.1 A big catch

That fish is huge! It is a swordfish being caught off the coast of Florida. This isn't a normal day's fishing down at the river bank – the fisherman has to be anchored into his seat to make sure that the fish doesn't drag him overboard.

The fisherman pulls against the fish to get it onto the boat. The pull is called a **force**. A force can be either a pull or a push. Twisting and bending happen when two pushes or pulls occur together. Force is measured in units called **Newtons**.

A force called **gravity** pulls the fish towards the Earth. Gravity pulls on the fish with a force of about 10 Newtons for every kilogramme of its weight.

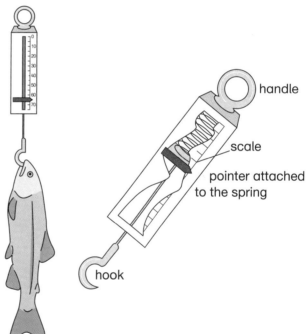

handle

scale

pointer attached to the spring

hook

G – force

Weight is normally measured in kilogrammes. This fish weighs over 60 kg. The fisherman will no doubt be bragging about his catch!

1 List some forces you experience every day.
2 Sort your list of forces into pushes and pulls.
3 Is gravity a push or a pull force?
4 Build a **Newton meter**. Test it with different weights to see how accurate it is.

force	Newton	gravity	Newton meter

16.2 Bungee

Some people actually pay money to tie an elastic rope to their legs and jump off a bridge hundreds of feet in the air. They call it bungee jumping. Would you be prepared to do it?

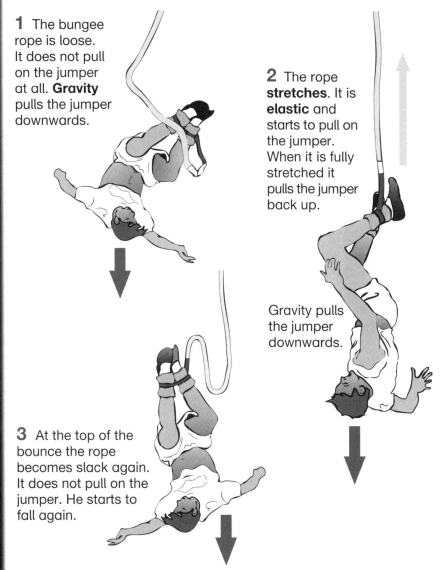

1 The bungee rope is loose. It does not pull on the jumper at all. **Gravity** pulls the jumper downwards.

2 The rope **stretches**. It is **elastic** and starts to pull on the jumper. When it is fully stretched it pulls the jumper back up.

Gravity pulls the jumper downwards.

3 At the top of the bounce the rope becomes slack again. It does not pull on the jumper. He starts to fall again.

1 What pulls the bungee jumper towards the ground?
2 What stops the bungee jumper hitting the ground?
3 Bungee ropes are elastic. What does elastic mean?
4 Is a bungee rope that is twice as thick as another also twice as strong? Test out your answer with elastic bands and weights.

gravity   stretch   elastic

16.3 Hit the ground

Parachutes let people and things fall to the ground slowly so they are not hurt or damaged. Sometimes parachutes are used to drop food and machines to isolated areas.

The parachute collects air. The air pushes up. This is called **air resistance**. Air resistance balances some of the pull of **gravity**. The parachute slows down the person's fall.

Gravity pulls the parachutist downwards.

1 List three sports which use gravity to pull things down.
2 If one parachute were twice the size of another, which one would land first?
3 Why do birds like vultures have big wings?
4 Why do you think that hang-gliders have big wings?

air resistance   gravity

16.4 Playing safe

Every year hundreds of children have accidents in playgrounds. Adventure playgrounds have lots more hazards than normal playgrounds, such as climbing frames and skateboard runs. Well-equipped skateboarders should wear a helmet, elbow pads and knee pads to prevent them from badly injuring themselves.

Gravity pulls you down when you fall. The harder the ground the more likely you are to hurt yourself. Soft surfaces are less painful to land on.

Pole vaulters use a lot of **energy** to jump over the bar.

The mattress absorbs a lot of energy when the person lands. The athlete sinks into the mattress and does not get hurt.

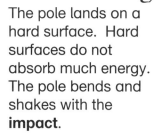

The pole lands on a hard surface. Hard surfaces do not absorb much energy. The pole bends and shakes with the **impact**.

1 Find out what kinds of surfaces your local playgrounds have. They may have more than one.
2 What kind of injuries do children get in adventure playgrounds?
3 Do you think that different kinds of surface can cause different types of injury?
4 Which surfaces are safest?
5 How else can children be protected when they are playing?

energy	impact

17.1 Eyes

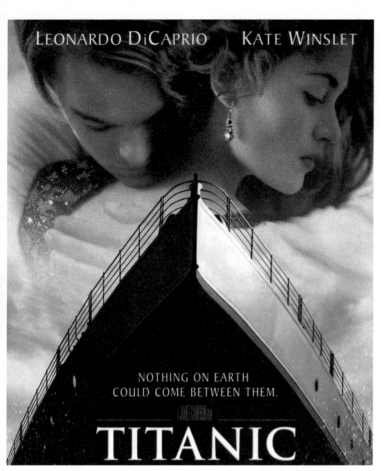

LEONARDO DiCAPRIO   KATE WINSLET

NOTHING ON EARTH
COULD COME BETWEEN THEM.

TITANIC

Titanic is one of the biggest movies of all time. It has made over 1.8 billion dollars in box office revenues since it was released in 1997, and it sold 1.8 million copies on video in its first week of sales in the UK alone. Just think that all of this money has been made from patterns of light bouncing off a flat white screen.

We see things when light goes into our eyes. Some things make their own light. We call these **luminous** objects. So, a light bulb and a candle flame are luminous objects. **Non-luminous** objects cannot make their own light. They reflect the light made by something else. The screen in a cinema is non-luminous. It reflects coloured light from the projector.

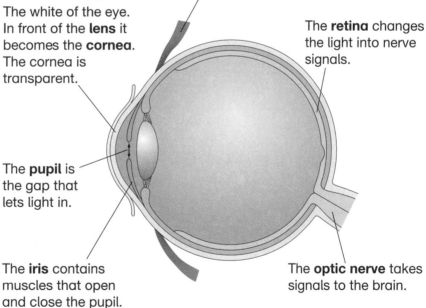

Muscles swivel the eyeball in its socket.

The white of the eye. In front of the **lens** it becomes the **cornea**. The cornea is transparent.

The **retina** changes the light into nerve signals.

The **pupil** is the gap that lets light in.

The **iris** contains muscles that open and close the pupil.

The **optic nerve** takes signals to the brain.

1 What does luminous mean?
2 Name three things that are luminous.
3 What does non-luminous mean?
4 Name three things that are non-luminous.
5 List the parts of the eye and explain what they do.

| luminous | non-luminous | lens | cornea | pupil |
| retina | optic nerve | iris | | |

Theatres

17.2 Reflections

Mirrors **reflect** light in a particular direction. A screen in a cinema reflects light in all directions. This page also reflects light in all directions. The mirrors in the photograph reflect the Sun's light into one small place – and it gets very hot.

We can use **rays** of light to investigate how mirrors reflect. A ray of light is a thin **beam**. We can see this beam when it touches a piece of white paper.

Mirrors are more complicated than they look. Mirror writing is writing that is the right way up but back to front – it makes no sense. But look at it in a mirror. The mirror flips the image, so the right side is on the left and the left on the right.

1 What is the difference between the way in which a mirror and a piece of white paper reflect light?
2 Use a light beam to find out how mirrors reflect light. Can you predict in which direction the beam will bounce off the mirror?
3 Write your name in mirror writing.
4 Draw a diagram to show how a flat mirror reflects a ray of light.

reflect   ray   beam

17.3 Light show

When light can't get through something, it creates a **shadow**. In Indonesia, shadow puppets are used to tell traditional stories. This is probably the oldest cinema in the world!

Light travels in straight lines. Mirrors **reflect** light. Lenses change the direction of light. The **lens** in your eye bends the rays of light to make an image on the **retina**. In a camera the lens bends the light to make an image on the film. In a film projector the lens bends the light to make an image on the screen.

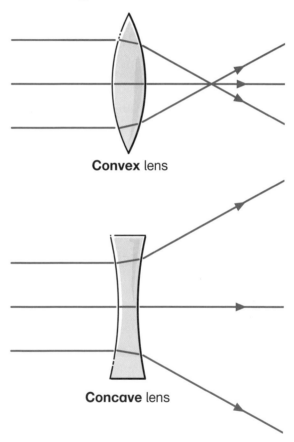

Convex lens

Concave lens

1 How many people do you think were needed to make the shadows in the photograph?
2 Make your own shadow puppet and test it.
3 How can you make the shadow bigger?
4 How can you make the shadow smaller?
5 Use a light box and different lenses to find out how much they change the light beam's direction.

| shadow | reflect | lens | retina | convex | concave |

17.4 Coloured lights

Sunlight is called white light. It contains all of the other colours mixed in together. A triangular piece of glass, called a **prism**, can sort these out into a **spectrum**. The prism lets all of the colours through but spreads them out.

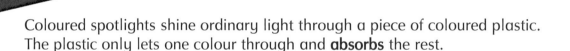

Coloured spotlights shine ordinary light through a piece of coloured plastic. The plastic only lets one colour through and **absorbs** the rest.

The red candle in the photograph looks red because it **reflects** red light. It absorbs all of the other colours. The white candle looks white because it reflects all colours of light.

Here is the same scene in red light. The white candle reflects the red light and so looks red. The blue candle absorbs the red light. There is no blue light to reflect so it looks black.

1. Draw a picture to show how you would use a torch and a piece of blue plastic to make a blue light.
2. Which candles look red in the second photograph? Why?
3. Which candle has the darkest colour in the second photograph? Why?
4. Draw a picture of a green apple on a white plate seen in white light.
5. Now draw the same picture seen in green light.

| prism | spectrum | absorb | reflect |

18.1 Rocket science

The most exciting journey of all time began in Cape Kennedy, Florida on July 16th 1969. Three men started their journey to the Moon.

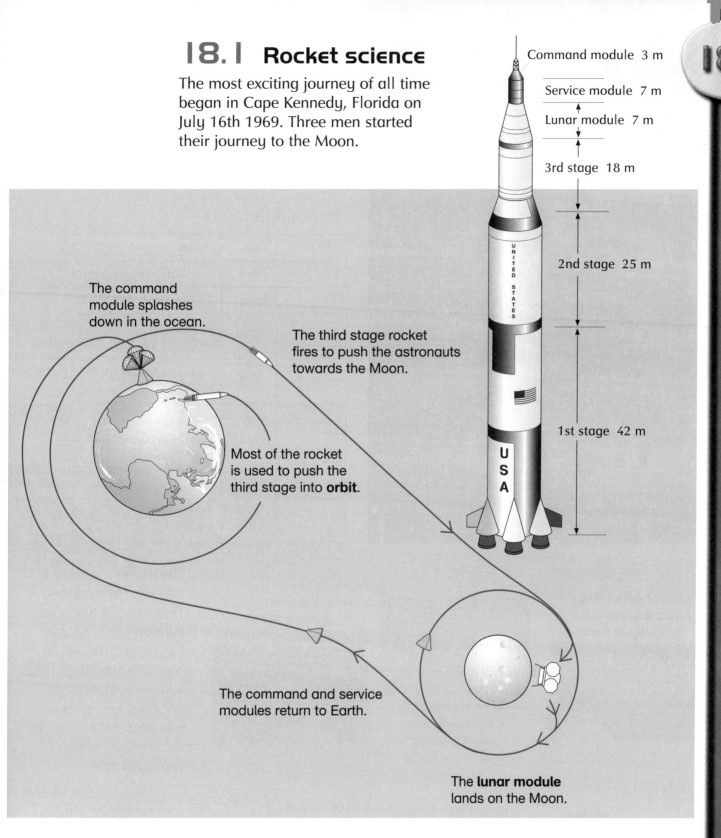

Command module 3 m

Service module 7 m

Lunar module 7 m

3rd stage 18 m

2nd stage 25 m

1st stage 42 m

The command module splashes down in the ocean.

The third stage rocket fires to push the astronauts towards the Moon.

Most of the rocket is used to push the third stage into **orbit**.

The command and service modules return to Earth.

The **lunar module** lands on the Moon.

1 Which part of the rocket landed on the Moon?
2 Which part of the rocket returned to Earth?
3 How tall is the command module?
4 Why is the rocket so large compared with the command module?

orbit   lunar module

18.2 Moon landing

After a five day flight, Apollo 11 reached the moon. At 2.56 in the morning of July 21st 1969, Neil Armstrong stepped onto the surface. His first words were heard all over the world 'That's one small step for man, a giant leap for mankind.'

The Apollo missions

Mission	Year	Notes
11	1969	First men on the Moon
12	1969	15 hours on the Moon
13	1970	Spacecraft struck by a meteorite. Landing cancelled.
14	1971	44 kg of Moon rock brought back.
15	1971	Lunar Rover is used – the first vehicle for driving on the Moon's surface.
16	1972	
17	1972	The last time men went to the Moon.

The Moon's gravity pulls the meteorite towards the surface.

When the meteorite hits the surface it produces a crater.

There is no wind or rain on the Moon so the crater is not worn away.

The Moon's surface is covered with **craters**. These are made when **meteorites** crash into the Moon. The Moon has no atmosphere and so the meteorites do not burn up as they fall. Meteorites may be the remains of an exploded star.

1 There is no atmosphere and therefore no wind or rain on the Moon. What would happen to the footprints left by an astronaut?
2 How many missions have there been to the moon since Apollo 11?
3 Which Apollo mission nearly ended in disaster?
4 Plan an investigation to find out how the size of a meteorite affects the size of a crater.

crater   meteorite

18.3 The space shuttle

The space shuttle is the first spaceship to be used more than once. It uses a rocket motor to propel it into **orbit** and then glides back to Earth just like a plane. Shuttles have now completed over 100 missions into space.

The shuttle needs a push to move it into orbit. The **booster rockets** supply the push. The shuttle is going forwards and upwards.

Once the shuttle reaches a certain height the rocket motors are switched off. The shuttle goes forwards but does not go any higher. The shuttle is falling around the Earth.

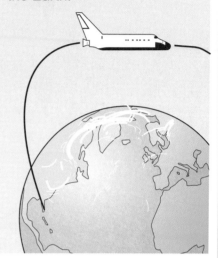

All the objects in the shuttle, including the astronauts, are falling at the same speed. Everything that is not fixed down floats around in the shuttle. Astronauts call this **weightlessness** conditions.

1 Why do astronauts float around inside the space shuttle when it is in orbit around the Earth?
2 What kind of experiments might be carried out on the space shuttle when it is in orbit?
3 What problems do you think the astronauts might have on a long mission?

| orbit | booster rocket | weightlessness |

18.4 The Moon

An object that **orbits** a planet is called a **satellite**. This satellite beams television signals into our homes. Satellites are also used for worldwide communication – and spying on other countries!

Satellites do not have to be man-made. The Earth has one natural satellite – the Moon. The Moon orbits the Earth every 28 days. It is a **non-luminous** object. When the Moon is shining in the night sky, we see rays of light from the Sun which have been reflected by the Moon.

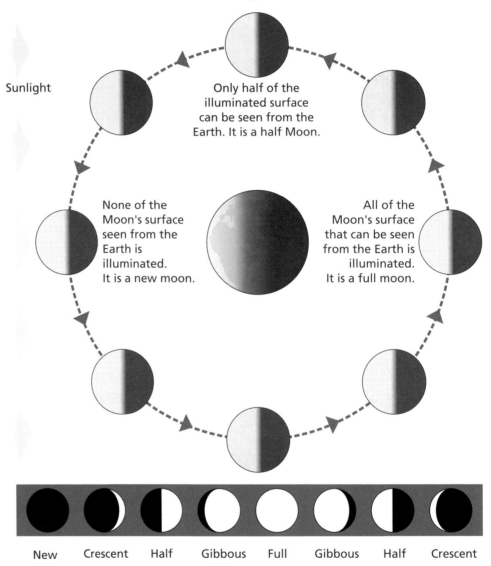

Sunlight

Only half of the illuminated surface can be seen from the Earth. It is a half Moon.

None of the Moon's surface seen from the Earth is illuminated. It is a new moon.

All of the Moon's surface that can be seen from the Earth is illuminated. It is a full moon.

| New | Crescent | Half | Gibbous | Full | Gibbous | Half | Crescent |

As the Moon orbits the Earth, it sometimes passes between the Earth and the Sun. This blocks out the sunlight causing a **solar eclipse**.

1 What is a satellite?
2 How many days does it take for the Moon to orbit the Earth?
3 How does a solar eclipse occur?
4 Find out how many other planets have their own moons.

| orbit | satellite | non-luminous | solar eclipse |

18.5 The solar system

The last successful Moon landing was in 1972. The next step, sending astronauts to **Mars** and bringing them back safely, is much more difficult. Although unmanned missions to Mars have been taking place since 1976, there have been no attempts made to send man to the 'red planet'. This is because, although it is the nearest **planet** to Earth, it is still around 380 million kilometres away!

Planet	Distance from Sun /million km	Diameter /km	Weight /Earth=1	Average surface temperature /°C	Time to travel round Sun /year
Mercury	58	4969	0.05	510	0.24
Venus	108	12200	0.8	480	0.62
Earth	150	12757	1.0	15	1.00
Mars	228	6800	0.1	-50	1.88
Jupiter	779	143600	318	-250	11.86
Saturn	1427	121000	95	-180	29.46
Uranus	2670	47000	15	-220	84.0
Neptune	4496	44600	17	-200	164.8
Pluto	5906	3000	0.06	-240	247.7

1 What is at the centre of our **solar system**?
2 How many planets are there in our solar system?
3 Which planet is closest to the Sun?
4 Which is the largest planet?
5 Why is it so much more difficult to send astronauts to Mars than it is to the Moon?

Mars   **planet**   **solar system**

abrasive	rough
absorb	to take in
acid	a chemical which turns litmus paper red
adaptation	something about an animal or plant that makes it suited to its environment
adapted	when an animal or plant is suited to its environment
afterbirth	the placenta and membranes that leave the mother's womb after the baby has been born
air resistance	air pushing against an object
airways	tubes that carry air when you breathe
alkali	a chemical which turns litmus paper blue
alloy	a mixture of two or more metals
alum	a chemical used to flameproof fabric
ammeter	meter used to measure electric current
amp	unit used to measure electric current
antenatal	before birth
antifreeze	liquid containing a chemical that makes its freezing point very low
anus	bottom end of the gut, where wastes are released from
apatosaurus	an extinct, plant-eating dinosaur
artery	blood vessel carrying blood away from the heart
artificial	something made by humans
atom	smallest part of an element
atrium	top chamber of the heart
attract	pull together
bacteria	microscopic living things
battery	device which stores chemical energy and gives out electricity
beam	line of light
bicarbonate of soda	a weak alkali used in indigestion tablets
biological	a washing powder that contains enzymes
birth weight	weight of a baby when it is born
bladder	body organ which stores urine
bleach	a cleaning chemical that kills germs and removes stains
bleeding	losing blood through a cut
blood pressure	the force of blood in the blood vessels
blood vessel	tube that carries blood in the body
boiling point	temperature at which something boils
booster rocket	the part of a space shuttle that pushes it into orbit
borax	a chemical used to flameproof fabric
breathing	taking air into and pushing air out of the lungs
bulb	produces light when electricity runs through it
capillary	thin-walled blood vessel that carries blood from arteries to veins
carbohydrate	chemical from food that gives you energy
carbon dioxide	a colourless gas that is found in very small amounts in the air; gas produced during respiration
cell	the basic unit of life
cell membrane	very thin, outer covering of a cell
chemical reaction	when two or more chemicals react together and bring about a change
circuit	a loop of electrical conductors
circulation	transport of blood around the body
coating	a layer spread over the surface of an object
coil	wire made into a springy shape
colour fast	the colour will not run or leak when wet
coma	deeply unconcious
compass	an instrument used for navigation
compound	substance made of two or more elements joined chemically
concave	a concave lens is thinnest in the middle
condense	to change from a gas or vapour to a liquid
conductor	a material that lets electricity flow through it
constipation	when it is difficult to release waste from the gut
contraction	rhythmic shortening of the muscles in the womb during labour
convex	a convex lens is fattest in the middle

copper	a cheap metal
cornea	clear part of the eye in front of the lens
corrode	reaction of a metal with the air; to rust
cramp	painful contraction of a muscle
crater	a hole in the Moon's surface caused by a meteorite
crude oil	unrefined oil
current	flow of electricity
cytoplasm	see-through, jelly-like substance in cells
decay	break down
de-icer	a spray that can be used on car windscreens to remove ice
detergent	a cleaning agent
diabetes	a disease that makes it hard to control your blood sugar level
diarrhoea	loose bowels
diet	what you eat and drink
digestion	the process of breaking down food in the gut
digestive enzyme	a substance in the gut that breaks large food molecules into smaller ones
dimmer	a switch that controls the resistance in an electrical circuit
dinosaur	extinct, giant reptile
displacement reaction	when one metal replaces another in a solution
dissolve	to disappear into a liquid
DNA	a chemical that carries genetic information
donor	the person who gives the organ in a transplant
dye	a substance that can change the colour of something else
earth	yellow and green wire in a three-pin plug, which electricity flows along if there is something wrong with the circuit
egg	female sex cell
elastic	when something changes its shape when a force acts on it and returns to its original shape when the force is removed
electricity	energy that flows through wires
electricity meter	meter used to measure the amount of electricity used
electrolysis	purifying a metal using electricity
electrolyte	liquid or paste inside a battery
electromagnet	a magnet that only works when electricity flows through it
electroplating	covering something with metal using electricity
element	substance containing only one type of atom
energy	the ability to do something
environment	the world that surrounds us
enzyme	a substance that changes the rate of a reaction
evaporation	when something changes from a liquid to a gas
excretion	gets rid of waste from the body
exercise	physical activity that keeps the body fit
expand	to get bigger
extinct	when a species of plant or animal has died out
fabric	a flat sheet used to make clothes
fat	chemical that gives energy and warmth
fertilise	one sperm cell joining with one egg cell
fever	a high temperature in the body
fibre	1 food that cannot be digested
	2 twisted to form a thread
flameproof	won't catch fire easily
force	push or pull
fossil	preserved remains of an animal or plant
freeze	change from a liquid to a solid
freezing point	the temperature at which a liquid freezes
friction	rubbing force which produces heat and wear and tear
fuse	safety device in a plug to stop electricity flowing
gas	not liquid or solid, a gas spreads out to fill all of the available space
gene	contains the information for particular characteristics
genitals	reproductive structures found outside of the body
gold	a precious metal

gold leaf	a flat sheet of gold
gravity	a force which pulls objects towards the Earth
growth	to get bigger
gut	the tube which takes food from the mouth to the anus
hard water	water with lots of dissolved substances in it that does not produce a lot of lather
hearing	the ability to hear sounds
height	how tall something is
host	the person who receives the organ in a transplant operation
hydrochloric acid	an acid found in your stomach
hydrogen	a colourless gas
hypothermia	when your body gets too cold to work properly
ichthyosaurus	an extinct, fish-like dinosaur
impact	the force with which one thing hits another
indicator	a substance that shows whether something is an acid or an alkali
indigestion	pain in your stomach caused by too much acid
indigo	a plant dye used to colour jeans blue
ingredients	items in a mixture
insoluble	a substance that will not dissolve
insulator	a material that does not let electricity through
insulin	a chemical which controls the amount of sugar in the blood
iris	coloured ring of muscle at the front of the eye
iron	a non-precious metal
Jurassic	the time when dinosaurs lived
kidney	body organ which cleans waste from the blood
large intestine	part of the gut which absorbs water
lens	1 curved piece of glass that bends light rays
	2 part of the eye that bends light rays to make an image on the retina
life process	function that happens in the body
lime	an alkaline substance used by farmers to neutralise their soil
limescale	white crystals left behind on taps and baths when water evaporates
liquid	not solid or gas, a liquid can flow
litmus paper	paper used to detect acids and alkalis
live wire	brown wire in a three-pin plug
loudspeaker	a speaker that uses electromagnets to work
lubricate	to make slippery
luminous	produces its own light
lunar module	the part of a space shuttle that lands on the Moon
magnesium	a metal that reacts with an acid
magnet	an object that attracts iron
magnetic	an object attracted to a magnet
magnetic field	the force field around a magnet
magnetic force	the force a magnet produces
mains supply	provides electricity
Mars	a planet in our solar system
melt	change from a solid to a liquid
melting point	the temperature at which a solid melts
meteorite	a rock from space
minerals	substances needed by the body in very small amounts
mixture	substance formed when ingredients are combined
mordant	substance that fixes a dye in a material
natural	not made by humans
neutral	1 neither acid nor alkaline
	2 blue wire in a three-pin plug
neutralisation	when an acid and an alkali react together to form a neutral solution
Newton	a unit used to measure force
Newton meter	an instrument used to measure pulling forces
nickel	a cheap metal
non-abrasive	smooth
non-luminous	something which reflects light but does not produce its own

non-slip	will stop you from slipping
nucleus	the part of the cell that controls all of the cell's functions
nutrition	food
optic nerve	carries messages from the eyes to the brain
orbit	to travel around a planet in a circular path
ovary	the female reproductive organ which produces eggs
oviduct	tube between the ovary and the womb that eggs move through
oxygen	a colourless gas needed for respiration
parallel circuit	an electrical circuit that has more than one path
penis	male sex organ located outside of the body
pH scale	measures the acidity or alkalinity of a solution
planet	a large mass that is in orbit around the Sun in a solar system
plasma	the liquid part of blood
platelets	small particles in the blood which help it to clot
platinum	a precious metal
plug	allows you to take electricity from the mains supply
pole	the ends of a magnet
power	the amount of energy that arrives at a point every second
prism	a piece of glass or plastic that splits rays of white light to produce a spectrum
properties	a characteristic that belongs to something
protein	a chemical needed by the body for growth and repair
pupil	the part of the eye that lets in light
purify	to make a substance pure
pylon	a large, metal structure used to carry electricity cables
ray	thin line of light
react	1 take part in a chemical change
	2 to respond to a stimulus
reaction	1 a chemical change
	2 a response to a stimulus
reactivity	how easily a chemical reacts
rechargeable	a battery that can have electricity put back into it and so be used again
rectum	the part of the gut which stores waste food until you go to the toilet
red blood cells	disc-shaped, oxygen-carrying cells in the blood
reflect	to bounce light back
reflex	an automatic response
repel	a force which pushes things apart
reproduce	to produce offspring
resin	a sticky substance produced by trees
resist	to try to stop
respiration	a chemical reaction that releases energy from food
retina	the part of the eye that detects light
saliva	a substance found in the mouth that breaks down starch
satellite	an object which is in orbit around a planet
scum	mark left around a bath in hard water areas
series circuit	an electrical circuit that has only one path
shadow	an area which light cannot get to
shiver	involuntary movement of muscles to produce heat
sight	to be able to see things
silver	a precious metal
small intestine	the part of the gut that breaks down and absorbs food
soap	a cleaning product
socket	allows you to take electricity from the mains supply
soft water	water that does not contain a lot of dissolved substances and produces a lot of lather
solar eclipse	when the Moon passes between Earth and the Sun, blocking the Sun's light
solar system	the Sun, and the planets that are in orbit around it
solid	not a gas or a liquid, has a fixed shape
soluble	will dissolve
solute	a solid that dissolves in a liquid

solution	a liquid which has a substance dissolved in it
solvent	a liquid which can dissolve a solid
spectrum	coloured light as seen in a rainbow
sperm	male sex cell
sperm duct	tube which carries the sperm from the testes to the penis
stain	a mark on fabric that is hard to remove
state	whether something is a solid, liquid or a gas
stimulus	a change in things around you that makes you react
store	put away to use later
strength	how strong something is
stretch	to make something longer
substance	what things are made from
sugar	used during respiration to produce energy, found in many foods
swamp	a waterlogged area
sweat	a watery liquid produced by the skin when it is hot
switch	used in an electrical circuit to turn something on and off
symbol	an image used to show something
temperature	a measure of how hot something is
terminal	one of the ends of a battery
testis	male reproductive organ that makes sperm
thread	several fibres twisted together, used to make fabrics
toxic	poisonous
transplant	to put a living organ into another person
turmeric	a natural dye used in Indian cooking, which can be used to detect acids and alkalis
tyrannosaurus	an extinct, meat-eating dinosaur
unit	a measure of electricity, electricity is sold in units
universal indicator (UI)	an indicator which shows the pH of a substance
urine	a pale, yellow liquid produced by the kidneys from water and waste in the blood
vagina	muscular tube that links the womb with the outside of a woman's body
valve	a flap that stops blood flowing backwards in the heart and blood vessels
vein	blood vessel that carries blood towards the heart
ventricle	lower chamber of the heart that pumps blood into the arteries
vibrate	move to and fro quickly while staying in one place
viscosity	thickness of a liquid
vitamins	substances needed by the body in very small amounts
voltage	the amount of energy a battery gives to the electricity it produces
voltmeter	used to measure voltage
water-resistant	lets only a small amount of water through
water vapour	water in the state of a gas
waterproof	lets no water through
waters breaking	when the sac of fluids protecting a baby bursts during labour
watts	unit of measurement for power
weight	how heavy something is
weightlessness	when gravity is not acting on objects, such as in space, and they float
white blood cells	colourless cells in the blood that protect the body from disease
windproof	lets no wind through
womb	muscular organ in a female where the baby develops
yarn	threads twisted together